REVISE EDEXCEL GCSE (9–1)
Mathematics
Foundation

PAST PAPERS Plus⁺

Series Consultant: Harry Smith

Author: Navtej Marwaha

Also available to support your revision:

Revise GCSE Study Skills Guide   9781447967071

The **Revise GCSE Study Skills Guide** is full of tried-and-trusted hints and tips for how to learn more effectively. It gives you techniques to help you achieve your best – throughout your GCSE studies and beyond!

Revise GCSE Revision Planner   9781447967828

The **Revise GCSE Revision Planner** helps you to plan and organise your time, step-by-step, throughout your GCSE revision. Use this book and wall chart to mastermind your revision.

For the full range of Pearson revision titles across KS2, KS3, GCSE, Functional Skills, AS/A Level and BTEC visit: www.pearsonschools.co.uk/revise

Contents

A small bit of small print

Pearson publishes Sample Assessment Material and the Specification on its website. This is the official content and this book should be used in conjunction with it. All the questions in this book were on the 2017 exam papers. The papers you will sit will be different, and these papers are provided for practice purposes only.

Using this book

This book has been created to help you prepare for your exam by familiarising yourself with the approach of the papers and the exam-style questions. Unlike the exam, however, each question has targeted hints, guidance and support in the margin to help you understand how to tackle them.

All questions also have fully worked solutions shown in the back of the book for you to refer to.

You may want to work through the papers at your own pace, to reinforce your knowledge of the topics and practise the skills you have gained throughout your course. Alternatively, you might want to practise completing a paper as if in an exam. If you do this, bear these points in mind:

- Use black ink or ballpoint pen.

- Answer all questions.

- Answer the questions in the spaces provided – there may be more space than you need.

- In a real exam, **you must show all your working out**.

- For each paper, check whether you can use a calculator or not. This is stated at the start of each paper. You **cannot** use a calculator for Paper 1.

- If your calculator does not have a π button, take the value of π to be 3.142 unless the question instructs otherwise.

- Diagrams are **not** accurately drawn, unless otherwise indicated in the question.

- The total number of marks available for each paper is 80 marks.

- You have 1 hour 30 minutes to complete each paper.

- The marks for each question are shown in brackets. Use this as a guide as to how much time to spend on each question.

- When checking your answer against the Answers at the back of the book, take note of how the marks for the question are awarded for working out, so you can see what you need to include in your answers.

Paper 1F: Non-calculator
Time allowed: 1 hour 30 minutes

Work out the value of 2^4

$2 \times 2 = 4 \times 2 = 8 \times 2 = 16 \times 2 = 32.$

................16................

(Total for Question 1 is 1 mark)

123 NUMBER

Revision Guide
Page 8

Hint

The **index** (4 here) tells you how many times to multiply the number by itself.

Write 7.264 51 correct to 3 decimal places.

7.264

................7.265................

(Total for Question 2 is 1 mark)

Revision Guide
Page 3

Hint

To round to 3 decimal places look at the digit in the fourth decimal place. If it is 5 or more round up. If it is less than 5 round down.

rn to page 125 for complete worked solutions to the questions on this page.

√xy² ALGEBRA

 Revision Guide
Pages 23, 30

Hint

For part (a), multiply the numbers first, then the terms.

Hint

First convert the mixed number into an improper fraction. Solve by getting x on its own on one side of the equation.

 % RATIO AND PROPORTION

 Revision Guide
Pages 55, 56

Hint

To convert a fraction into a percentage. multiply by 100.

---

3 (a) Simplify $7 \times e \times f \times 8$

$7 \times 8 = 56$

...........$56ef$...........

(b) Solve $\dfrac{x}{5} = 2\dfrac{1}{2}$

$x = $ ....

(Total for Question 3 is 2 mark

---

4 Write $\dfrac{4}{5}$ as a percentage.

$\dfrac{4}{5} \times 100 = 80$ $\dfrac{\cancel{400}}{\cancel{500}}$

........80........

(Total for Question 4 is 1 mar

Turn to page 125 for complete worked solutions to the questions on this pag

Work out 60% of 70

$$35 + 7 = 42$$

$$50\% = 35$$

$$10\% = 7$$

.....42.....

(Total for Question 5 is 2 marks)

RATIO AND PROPORTION

Revision Guide Page 57

LEARN IT!

To find a percentage of an amount, divide the percentage by 100, then multiply by the amount.

Sammy spins a fair 4-sided spinner.

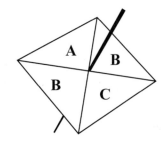

(i) On the probability scale, mark with a cross (×) the probability that the spinner will land on **B**.

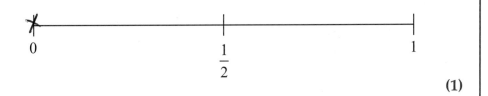

(1)

(ii) On the probability scale, mark with a cross (×) the probability that the spinner will land on **F**.

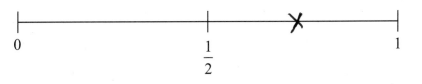

(1)

(Total for Question 6 is 2 marks)

PROBABILITY AND STATISTICS

Revision Guide Page 128

Hint

Letter B is on 2 of the 4 sections. Write this as a fraction, then work out its position on the probability scale.

LEARN IT!

Probability =

$$\frac{\text{number of successful outcomes}}{\text{total number of possible outcomes}}$$

LEARN IT!

Does the spinner have the letter F?

The **probability of an impossible event** is 0.

rn to page 125 for complete worked solutions to the questions on this page.

3

¹2³ NUMBER

Revision Guide
Page 7

Revision Guide Page 7

Hint

Convert the change into pounds and include in your calculation.

Problem solved!

- Work out the cost of 2 packets of bread rolls.
- Subtract the cost of the bread rolls, ketchup and the change given from £10.
- Divide your answer by 3 to find the cost of one packet of sausages.

Revision Guide
Page 14

Revision Guide Page 14

Hint

To subtract fractions, write them as equivalent fractions with a **common denominator**.

LEARN IT!

You can find **equivalent fractions** by multiplying or dividing the numerator and the denominator by the same number.

---

7 Fahima buys

    2 packets of bread rolls costing £1.50 for each packet

    1 bottle of ketchup costing £1.60

    3 packets of sausages

Fahima pays with a £10 note.

She gets 30p change.

Fahima works out that one packet of sausages costs £2.30

Is Fahima right?

You must show how you get your answer.

(Total for Question 7 is 3 marks)

8 (a) Work out $\dfrac{5}{8} \times \dfrac{3}{4}$

....

(b) Work out $\dfrac{2}{3} - \dfrac{1}{4}$

....

(Total for Question 8 is 3 marks)

Turn to page 125 for complete worked solutions to the questions on this page

Sean works for a company.

His normal rate of pay is £12 per hour.

When Sean works more than 8 hours a day, he is paid overtime for each hour he works more than 8 hours.

Sean's rate of overtime pay per hour is $1\frac{1}{4}$ times his normal rate of pay per hour.

On Monday Sean worked for 10 hours.

Work out the total amount of money Sean earned on Monday.

¹2³ NUMBER

Revision Guide
Pages 4, 5, 15

Problem solved!

- Work out the pay for 8 hours at the normal rate.
- Work out the number of overtime hours.
- Convert the overtime rate to an improper fraction.
- Work out the pay for the overtime.
- Add the answers to work out the total amount earned.

£ ....

(Total for Question 9 is 4 marks)

A farmer has 20 boxes of eggs.

There are 6 eggs in each box.

Write, as a ratio, the number of eggs in two boxes to the total number of eggs.

Give your answer in its simplest form.

% RATIO AND PROPORTION

Revision Guide
Page 59

Hint

Work out the number of eggs in two boxes and the total number of eggs. Then write a ratio in the order stated in the question.

Watch out!

Cancel down to the simplest form.

....

(Total for Question 10 is 2 marks)

rn to page 126 for complete worked solutions to the questions on this page.

 **ALGEBRA**

 Revision Guide
Page 34

Hint

Write down the number
of square tiles in each
pattern number and
continue the sequence
until the sixth pattern.

LEARN IT!

These numbers are
called **square numbers**.

Hint

Write down the number
of circular tiles needed
for each pattern
number and look for a
sequence.

LEARN IT!

You need to know the
properties of numbers:
• even × even = even
• odd × odd = odd
• even × odd = even
• odd × even = even

Explore

You can use simple
properties of numbers,
e.g. odd × odd = odd,
in much more
complicated proofs
in algebra.

---

11 A sequence of patterns is made from circular tiles
   and square tiles

   Here are the first three patterns in the sequence.

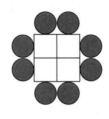   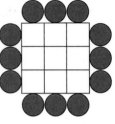

   pattern number 1   pattern number 2   pattern number 3

   (a) How many square tiles are needed to make pattern
      number 6?

      ....

      (

   (b) How many circular tiles are needed to make pattern
      number 20?

      ....

      (

   Derek says,

      "When the pattern number is odd, an odd number of
      square tiles is needed to make the pattern."

   (c) Is Derek right?

      You must give reasons for your answer.

   ....

   ....

   ....

      (

(Total for Question 11 is 6 mark

Turn to page 126 for complete worked solutions to the questions on this page

2 There are only 7 blue pens, 4 green pens and 6 red pens in a box.

One pen is taken at random from the box.

Write down the probability that this pen is blue.

....

(Total for Question 12 is 2 marks)

3 The diagram shows a tree and a man.

The man is of average height.

The tree and the man are drawn to the same scale.

(a) Write down an estimate for the real height, in metres, of the man.

.... metres

(1)

(b) Find an estimate for the real height, in metres, of the tree.

.... metres

(2)

(Total for Question 13 is 3 marks)

rn to page 126 for complete worked solutions to the questions on this page.

 PROBABILITY AND STATISTICS

 Revision Guide Page 127

LEARN IT!

Probability =

$$\frac{\text{number of successful outcomes}}{\text{total number of possible outcomes}}$$

 GEOMETRY AND MEASURES

 Revision Guide Page 98

LEARN IT!

You need to know **common metric units** for length, mass (weight) and capacity (volume).

Problem solved!

1. Use a ruler to measure the height of the man and the height of the tree on the diagram.

3. Use these to work out the **scale factor**.

3. Multiply your estimate of the man's real height by the scale factor to estimate the real height of the tree.

Watch out!

Make sure you write down every stage of the calculation.

Revision Guide
Page 118

Hint

To work out an angle of each sector in a pie chart, first work out the angle that represents one student. Then multiply that angle by the number of students in each category to find the angle for that sector.

LEARN IT!

A circle is 360° so the sectors in a pie chart add up to 360°.

Watch out!

Use a **protractor** to measure and draw the angles.

14 Year 9 students from Halle School were asked to choose one language to study.

The table shows information about their choices.

Language	Number of students	
French	56	
Spanish	40	
German	24	

(a) Draw an accurate pie chart to show this information.

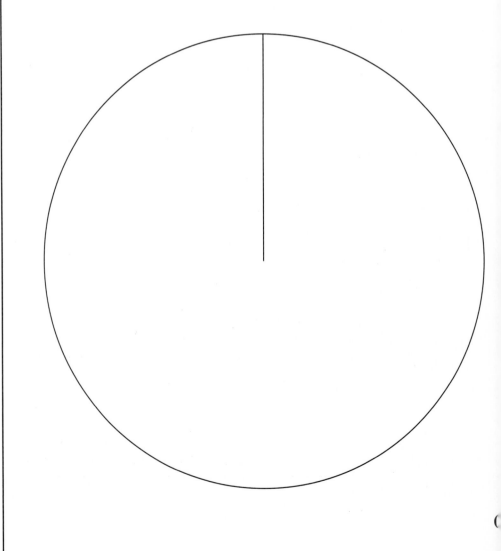

Turn to page 126 for complete worked solutions to the questions on this page

Year 9 students from Lowry School were also asked to choose one language to study.

This accurate pie chart shows information about their choices.

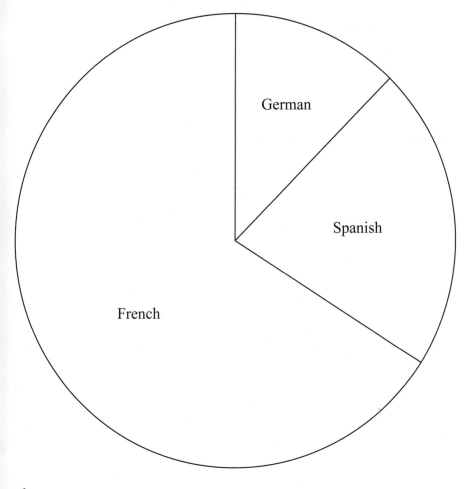

Hint

To compare the sectors in different pie charts you need to know the total **number** that each pie chart represents.

LEARN IT!

A pie chart gives information about relative **proportions**.

Watch out!

When a sector of one pie chart has a greater angle than a sector of a second pie chart, it does **not** mean that the first sector represents more people than the second. This is because the angle of the sector depends upon the total number of people that each pie chart shows.

Shameena says,

"The pie chart shows that French was chosen by more Year 9 students at Lowry School than at Halle School."

(b) Is Shameena right?

You must explain your answer.

....

....

(1)

(Total for Question 14 is 4 marks)

rn to page 127 for complete worked solutions to the questions on this page.

GEOMETRY
AND MEASURES

Revision Guide
Page 79

LEARN IT!

Area of triangle
$= \dfrac{\text{base} \times \text{height}}{2}$
Area of rectangle
$= \text{length} \times \text{width}$

Problem solved!

1. Work out the area of the triangle.

2. Write down an expression for the area of the rectangle.

3. Set up an equation showing that the area of the rectangle is 6 times the area of the triangle.

4. Solve the equation for w.

$\sqrt{xy^2}$ **ALGEBRA**

Revision Guide
Page 25

Hint

Remember that at means $a \times t$.

Substitute the numbers into the formula then work out the answer. Write down each step and take care when you multiply by a negative number.

---

15 Here are a triangle and a rectangle.

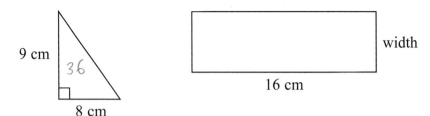

9 cm

36

8 cm

width

16 cm

The area of the rectangle is 6 times the area of the triangle.

Work out the width of the rectangle.

9, 18, 27, 36, 45, 54, 63, 72

$72 \div 2 = 36$

$\begin{array}{r} 3\ 3\ 6 \\ \times\ \ \ 6 \\ \hline 2\ 7\ 6 \end{array}$ 276

$\begin{array}{r} 0\ 1 \\ 16\overline{)2\,{}^2 7\,{}^1 6} \end{array}$

16, 32, 48,

.... cm

(Total for Question 15 is 4 marks

---

16 $v = u + at$

$u = 1 \qquad a = -3 \qquad t = \dfrac{1}{2}$

Work out the value of v.

$u -$

$1 + -3 \times 1/2$

$v = ...2 \cdot 5......$

(Total for Question 16 is 2 marks

Turn to page 127 for complete worked solutions to the questions on this page

5 tins of soup have a total weight of 1750 grams.

4 tins of soup and 3 packets of soup have a total weight of 1490 grams.

Work out the total weight of 3 tins of soup and 2 packets of soup.

 NUMBER

Revision Guide
Pages 4, 5

Hint

Read the question carefully. Do one step at a time, writing down your working.

Problem solved!

Plan your strategy:
- work out the weight of one tin of soup
- use this to work out the weight of one packet of soup
- work out the weight of 3 tins of soup and 2 packets of soup.

.... grams

(Total for Question 17 is 4 marks)

rn to page 127 for complete worked solutions to the questions on this page.

GEOMETRY AND MEASURES

 Revision Guide Page 104

Hint

You can approximate values to 1 significant figure when estimating. You can also approximate π to 1 significant figure.

LEARN IT!

Area of circle = πr^2

Problem solved!

Work out the number of boxes needed by:
• working out the area of the garden
• dividing this by the area covered by one box of grass seed.

Hint

Think about how the different approximations affect the answer.

Watch out!

You need to explain clearly why more or fewer boxes will be needed.

---

18 Balena has a garden in the shape of a circle of radius 10 m.
He is going to cover the garden with grass seed to make a lawn.

Grass seed is sold in boxes.
Each box of grass seed will cover 46 m² of garden.

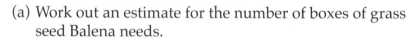

10 m

Balena wants to cover all the garden with grass seed.

(a) Work out an estimate for the number of boxes of grass seed Balena needs.

You must show your working.

....

(

(b) Is your estimate for part (a) an underestimate or an overestimate?

Give a reason for your answer.

....

....

....

(

(Total for Question 18 is 5 mark

Turn to page 127 for complete worked solutions to the questions on this pag

19 (a) Solve $4(x - 5) = 18$

$x =$ ....

(2)

$-3 < t \leqslant 2$

t is an integer.

(b) Write down all the possible values of t.

....

(2)

(Total for Question 19 is 4 marks)

20 Azmol is paid £1500 per month.

He is going to get a 3% increase in the amount of money he is paid.

Work out how much money Azmol will be paid per month after the increase.

£ ....

(Total for Question 20 is 2 marks)

rn to page 128 for complete worked solutions to the questions on this page.

 ALGEBRA

Revision Guide
Pages 31, 32

Hint

First write down all the integers between −3 and 2. Then look carefully at the inequality signs in the statement to see if any numbers are not included.

LEARN IT!

$a < n \leqslant b$ means that a **is not** included and b **is** included.

 RATIO AND PROPORTION

Revision Guide
Page 57

Hint

Calculate 3% of 1500 as $\frac{3}{100} \times 1500$

Hint

Azmol's pay is **increased** so his new pay will be greater than his pay at the start.

Watch out!

Make sure you add the percentage increase to the initial amount.

PROBABILITY AND STATISTICS

Revision Guide
Page 119

LEARN IT!

An **outlier** is a value that does not fit the pattern of the data.

Hint

You might find it helpful to circle the outlier.

LEARN IT!

Always write coordinates as (x, y).

Hint

You need to describe **correlation** using correct mathematical language such as 'positive', 'negative' or 'no correlation'.

21 The scatter graph shows the maximum temperature and the number of hours of sunshine in fourteen British towns on one day.

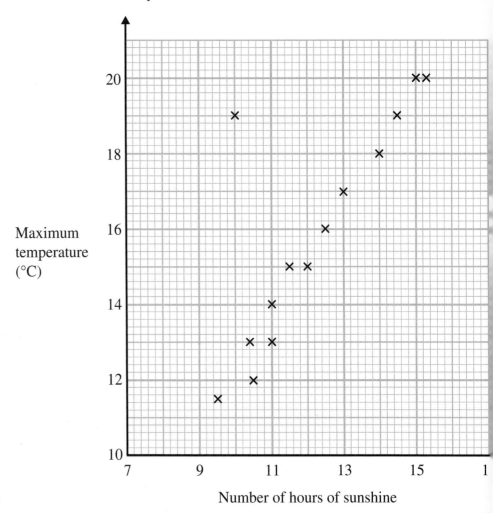

Number of hours of sunshine

One of the points is an outlier.

(a) Write down the coordinates of this point.

(................................. , ...

(b) For all the other points write down the type of correlation.

....

Turn to page 128 for complete worked solutions to the questions on this page

On the same day, in another British town, the maximum temperature was 16.4°C.

(c) Estimate the number of hours of sunshine in this town on this day.

.... hours

(2)

Hint

Draw a line of best fit on the graph. Read across from 16.4 on the vertical axis to your line of best fit. Then go down to the horizontal axis to read off a value for the number of hours of sunshine.

A weatherman says,

"Temperatures are higher on days when there is more sunshine."

(d) Does the scatter graph support what the weatherman says?

Give a reason for your answer.

....

....

(1)

(Total for Question 21 is 5 marks)

Hint

You need to answer 'yes' or 'no' and give a reason. Your reason must be in the context of the question.

Express 56 as the product of its prime factors.

....

(Total for Question 22 is 2 marks)

¹₂³ NUMBER

 Revision Guide Page 12

Problem solved!

Use a factor tree to find prime factors:
• choose a factor pair of the number
• for each factor, keep finding factor pairs
• circle the prime factors as you go
• continue until each branch ends with a prime number
• write the answer as a product.

rn to page 128 for complete worked solutions to the questions on this page.

NUMBER

Revision Guide
Pages 5, 7

Hint

Use long multiplication.

Hint

Ignore the decimal points and multiply the numbers.
Count the number of decimal places in the calculation. Write the decimal point in your answer so that it has the same number of decimal places.

Hint

Check your answer by estimating 55 × 4.

23 Work out 54.6×4.3

....

(Total for Question 23 is 3 marks

16

$\sqrt{xy^2}$ **ALGEBRA**

Revision Guide
Page 43

4

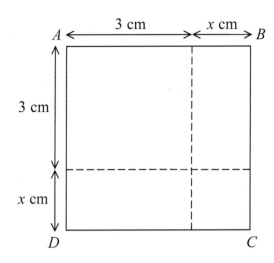

The area of square $ABCD$ is 10 cm².

Show that $x^2 + 6x = 1$

(Total for Question 24 is 3 marks)

LEARN IT!

Area of a square
= length × width

Problem solved!

Plan your strategy:
• start by finding an expression for the area of the whole square by multiplying expressions for the length and width
• put brackets around each expression before you multiply them
• expand the brackets
• put your expression equal to 10
• gather all the number terms on the right-hand side.

Watch out!

Write down all your steps, showing your working clearly.

Explore

An expression in the form $x^2 + 2ax + a^2$ is called a **perfect square** because it factorises to give $(x + a)(x + a) = (x + a)^2$.

Turn to page 129 for complete worked solutions to the questions on this page.

 GEOMETRY AND MEASURES

Revision Guide
Page 90

Problem solved!

1. The frame is a rectangle so use Pythagoras' theorem to work out the length of the diagonal.

2. Find the total length of the frame.

3. Multiply the total length by the weight per metre to find the total weight.

LEARN IT!

Pythagoras' theorem states:

$a^2 + b^2 = c^2$

LEARN IT!

You need to know the **square numbers** up to 15^2 and their corresponding square roots.

 **Explore**

Pythagoras was a Greek philosopher and mathematician who lived in the 6th century BCE. His teachings influenced later Greek thinkers such as Plato and Aristotle.

25 This rectangular frame is made from 5 straight pieces of metal.

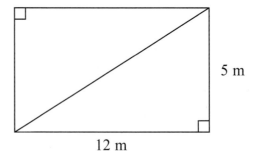

5 m

12 m

The weight of the metal is 1.5 kg per metre.

Work out the total weight of the metal in the frame.

.... k

(Total for Question 25 is 5 mark

Turn to page 129 for complete worked solutions to the questions on this page

26 The equation of the line L_1 is $y = 3x - 2$

The equation of the line L_2 is $3y - 9x + 5 = 0$

Show that these two lines are parallel.

(Total for Question 26 is 2 marks)

  **ALGEBRA**

Revision Guide
Page 37

LEARN IT!

The **equation of a straight line** has the form $y = mx + c$, where m is the gradient.

Hint

The gradients of parallel lines are equal. Find the gradients of both lines and compare them. Rearrange L_2 so that it is in the form $y = mx + c$.

Watch out!

Be careful with the signs when you rearrange equations.

urn to page 129 for complete worked solutions to the questions on this page.

Revision Guide
Page 112

Hint

Vectors have direction.

Hint

O is the midpoint of $\overrightarrow{DB}$ so the length from D to B is twice the length from O to B in the same direction.

Hint

Follow the path from A to B. If you go backwards along a vector you add the negative of that vector (that is, subtract that vector).

Hint

Can you express $\overrightarrow{AD}$ in terms of the vectors you have already found?

Hint

Simplify vectors in the same way as you simplify an algebraic expression (by collecting like terms).

27

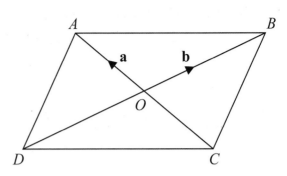

$ABCD$ is a parallelogram.

The diagonals of the parallelogram intersect at O.

$\overrightarrow{OA} = \mathbf{a}$ and $\overrightarrow{OB} = \mathbf{b}$

(a) Find, in terms of $\mathbf{b}$, the vector $\overrightarrow{DB}$.

....

(

(b) Find, in terms of $\mathbf{a}$ and $\mathbf{b}$, the vector $\overrightarrow{AB}$.

....

(

(c) Find, in terms of $\mathbf{a}$ and $\mathbf{b}$, the vector $\overrightarrow{AD}$.

....

(

(Total for Question 27 is 3 mark

TOTAL FOR PAPER 1F IS 80 MARK

Turn to page 129 for complete worked solutions to the questions on this page

Paper 2F: Calculator
Time allowed: 1 hour 30 minutes

(a) Simplify $5p - 3p + p$

....

(1)

(b) Simplify $m^3 + m^3$

....

(1)

(c) Simplify $10 + 3c + 5d - 7c + d$

....

(2)

(Total for Question 1 is 4 marks)

Write 56.78 correct to one significant figure.

....

(Total for Question 2 is 1 mark)

...rn to page 130 for complete worked solutions to the questions on this page.

 ALGEBRA

 Revision Guide
Page 22

Hint

How many m^3 are there in total?

Watch out!

$m^3 + m^3 \neq m^6$

Hint

Group the c terms together and the d terms together.

Watch out!

The sign (+ or −) goes with the term that follows it.

NUMBER

 Revision Guide
Page 3

Problem solved!

To round a number to one significant figure look at the second digit:
• if it is 5 or more, add 1 to the first digit (round up)
• if it is less than 5, do not change it (round down).

PROBABILITY AND STATISTICS

Revision Guide
Page 117

Turn to page 130 for complete worked solutions to the questions on this page

3　A teacher asks the students in Year 6 what type of transport they use to get to school.

The dual bar chart shows some of the results.

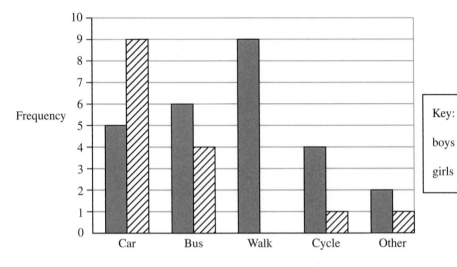

(a) What is the most popular type of transport used by the boys?

....

(

Hint

Use the key. Look for the highest bar for the boys.

7 girls walk to school.

(b) Show this information on the dual bar chart.

(

Hint

Use a ruler and a pencil to draw the bar.

More of the students get to school by car than by bus.

(c) How many more?

Hint

Work out the total number of students who travel by car and by bus. Find the difference between these two numbers.

....

(

The number of students in Year 5 is the same as the number of students in Year 6.

(d) What is the total number of students in Years 5 and 6?

Hint

Work out the total number of students in Year 6 and then multiply by 2.

....

(

(Total for Question 3 is 5 mark

4 Here are four fractions.

$$\frac{2}{5} \qquad \frac{11}{30} \qquad \frac{1}{2} \qquad \frac{7}{15}$$

Write these fractions in order of size.
Start with the smallest fraction.

....

(Total for Question 4 is 2 marks)

 NUMBER

Revision Guide
Page 13

Hint

To compare fractions
write them as
equivalent fractions
with a **common
denominator** (the same
number beneath the
line in a fraction).

LEARN IT!

You can find **equivalent
fractions** by multiplying
or dividing the
numerator and the
denominator by the
same number.

Hint

Once all the fractions
have the same
denominator, compare
their numerators and
number them in order
of increasing size.
Then write the **original**
fractions in order.

Watch out!

The question tells
you to start with the
smallest fraction.

urn to page 130 for complete worked solutions to the questions on this page.

PROBABILITY AND STATISTICS

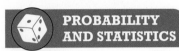
Revision Guide
Page 116

Hint

Check if the tallies match the frequencies.

Hint

Look at the key. What does ◖ represent?

5   David sells CDs in a shop.

The tally chart shows information about the number of CDs David sold on Monday, on Tuesday and on Wednesday.

	Tally	**Frequency**
Monday	卌 卌 |||	12
Tuesday	卌 卌 卌 |||	18
Wednesday	卌 |||	8

(a) Write down **one** thing that is wrong with the tally chart.

....

....

(1

David drew this pictogram to show the information for Tuesday and Wednesday.

Tuesday	◑ ◑ ◑ ◑ ◑
Wednesday	◑ ◑ ◖

Key: ◑ represents 3 CDs

(b) Write down **one** thing that is wrong with this pictogram.

....

....

(1

(Total for Question 5 is 2 marks

Turn to page 130 for complete worked solutions to the questions on this page.

There are 495 coins in a bottle.

$\frac{1}{3}$ of the coins are £1 coins.

124 of the coins are 50p coins.

The rest of the coins are 20p coins.

Work out the total value of the 495 coins.

£ ....

(Total for Question 6 is 4 marks)

1₂³ NUMBER

Revision Guide
Pages 7, 13

Hint

Work in consistent units; use either pounds or pence.

Problem solved!

Plan your strategy:
- work out the number of £1 coins and their value
- work out the number of 50p coins and their value
- work out the number of 20p coins from the total number of coins
- work out the value of the 20p coins
- find the total value of all the coins by adding the values of each type of coin.

Watch out!

Write down every step of your working, even if you are using a calculator.

Watch out!

Check your final answer – does it look sensible given the numbers and value of the coins?

Turn to page 131 for complete worked solutions to the questions on this page.

 PROBABILITY AND STATISTICS

Revision Guide
Page 128

LEARN IT!

P(event **doesn't occur**)
= 1 − P(**event occurs**)

 **NUMBER**

Revision Guide
Pages 8, 11

LEARN IT!

When a number is multiplied by itself, the answer is a **square number**.

Hint

Write the times tables for 4 and for 6. Look for a number that is in both lists.

LEARN IT!

A **prime number** has exactly two factors: 1 and itself.

---

7 The probability that a new fridge has a fault is 0.015.

What is the probability that a new fridge does **not** have a fault?

....

(Total for Question 7 is 1 mark

---

8 Here is a list of numbers.

21 22 23 24 25 26 27 28 29

(a) From the numbers in the list, write down a square number.

....
(1

(b) From the numbers in the list, write down a number that is a multiple of **both** 4 and 6.

....
(1

(c) Write down all the prime numbers in the list.

....
(1

(Total for Question 8 is 3 marks

Turn to page 131 for complete worked solutions to the questions on this page.

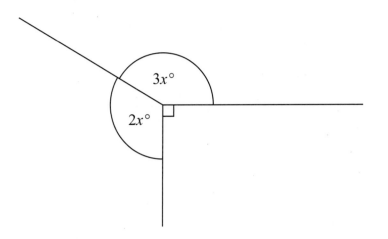

Find the value of x.

 GEOMETRY AND MEASURES

 Revision Guide Page 73

LEARN IT!

A **right angle** ⌐ is 90°.

Angles around a point add up to 360°.

Hint

Set up an equation in terms of x. Make this expression equal to 360 and solve for x.

Watch out!

Remember that diagrams are **not** accurately drawn unless stated.

....

(Total for Question 9 is 3 marks)

urn to page 131 for complete worked solutions to the questions on this page.

27

Revision Guide
Pages 4, 5

Hint

Suha does not need to **buy** all the packs needed from Stationery World because she will get some packs for free.

Problem solved!

1. Work out the number of packs needed from Letters2send and the cost of these.

2. Work out the number of packs needed from Stationery World.

3. Work out how many packs must be bought from Stationery World and how many will be free in order to get the total needed.

4. Work out the cost of the packs bought from Stationery World.

5. Compare the costs.

6. Answer the question by stating where Suha should buy her envelopes.

---

10 Suha is going to buy 150 envelopes.

Here is some information about the cost of envelopes in two shops.

Letters2send	Stationery World
Pack of 25 envelopes for £3.49	Pack of 10 envelopes for £2.10 Buy 2 packs get 1 pack free

Suha wants to buy the envelopes as cheaply as possible.

Which shop should Suha buy the 150 envelopes from?
You must show how you get your answer.

(Total for Question 10 is 4 marks)

Turn to page 131 for complete worked solutions to the questions on this page.

1 You can use this graph to change between inches and centimetres.

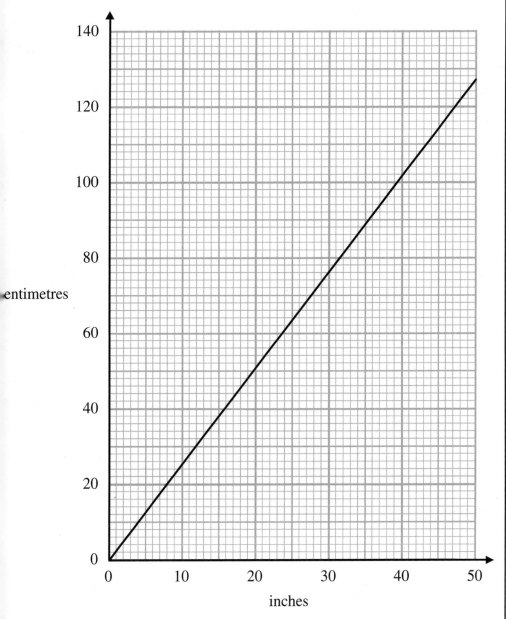

 ALGEBRA

 Revision Guide Page 40

Hint

Use a sharp pencil and a ruler to draw a line across from 74 on the vertical axis to the graph line and then down to the horizontal axis.

(a) Change 74 cm to inches.

.... inches

(1)

urn to page 132 for complete worked solutions to the questions on this page.   **29**

Hint

The graph on Page 29 is not large enough so you will need to find a factor of the height and scale up.

Problem solved!

1. Convert Daniel's height to inches.

2. Find a useful factor of the height.

3. Use the graph to convert the useful factor from inches to cm.

4. Multiply this answer by the appropriate number to scale up to the full height.

 NUMBER

Revision Guide
Page 16

Hint

Use your calculator to work out the value of the numerator and the denominator separately. Write these values down.

Explore

Use the fraction button on your calculator and enter the numbers in one go. Remember to apply **BIDMAS**, the correct priority (order) of operations.

Daniel's height is 6 feet 3 inches.

1 foot = 12 inches

(b) What is Daniel's height in centimetres?

.... centimetre

(3

(Total for Question 11 is 4 marks

---

12 Find the value of $\dfrac{\sqrt{13.4 - 1.5}}{(6.8 + 0.06)^2}$

Write down all the figures on your calculator display.

....

(Total for Question 12 is 2 marks

 Turn to page 132 for complete worked solutions to the questions on this page.

3

GEOMETRY AND MEASURES

Revision Guide
Page 87, 88

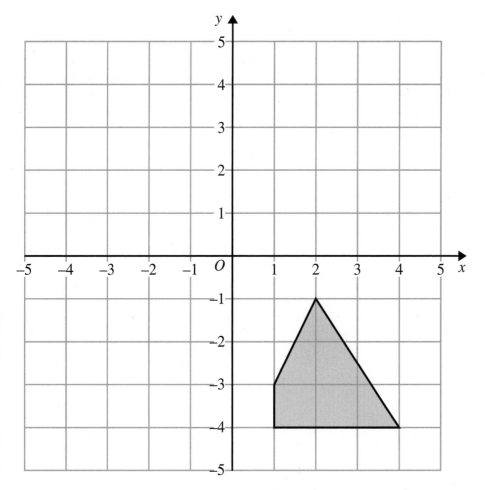

(a) Rotate shape **A** 90° clockwise about centre *O*.

(2)

Problem solved!

Draw the shape on tracing paper.
- Put your pencil on the tracing paper at the origin (*O*).
- Rotate the tracing paper 90° clockwise.
- Mark the vertices of the shape on the grid.
- Draw straight lines connecting the vertices to draw the shape on the grid.

Watch out!

Read the question carefully to make sure you rotate the shape in the correct direction and by the right amount.

Turn to page 132 for complete worked solutions to the questions on this page.

LEARN IT!

There are four **types of transformation:** enlargement, reflection, rotation and translation.

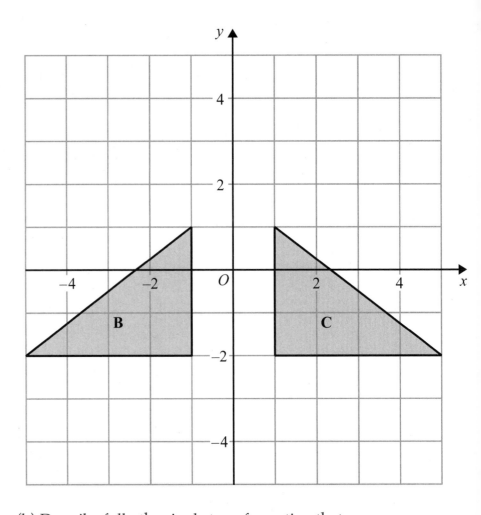

Hint

To describe this transformation fully, you need to write the name of the transformation **and** give an equation of a line.

(b) Describe fully the single transformation that maps triangle **B** onto triangle **C**.

....

....

(2

(Total for Question 13 is 4 marks

Turn to page 132 for complete worked solutions to the questions on this page.

4 (a) Factorise $5 - 10m$

....
(1)

(b) Factorise fully $2a^2b + 6ab^2$

....
(2)

(Total for Question 14 is 3 marks)

5 (a) Write 4.7×10^{-1} as an ordinary number.

....
(1)

(b) Work out the value of $(2.4 \times 10^3) \times (9.5 \times 10^5)$

Give your answer in standard form.

....
(2)

(Total for Question 15 is 3 marks)

urn to page 133 for complete worked solutions to the questions on this page.

√x̄y² **ALGEBRA**

Revision Guide
Page 29

Hint

To **factorise** an expression, take out any common factors of all the terms.

¹2³ **NUMBER**

Revision Guide
Pages 17, 18

Hint

You can enter this in one go on your calculator using the $\times 10^x$ button, but make sure you write down all your working.

LEARN IT!

You write a number in **standard form** as $n \times 10^x$ where $1 \le n < 10$ and x is an integer (whole number).

GEOMETRY AND MEASURES

Revision Guide
Pages 98, 99

Problem solved!

1. Use a ruler and compasses to construct a perpendicular bisector of the line segment BC.

2. Then set your compasses at 2.5 cm and draw an arc based on A so that it cuts the perpendicular bisector.

Hint

Never rub out your construction lines.

LEARN IT!

All the points on a **perpendicular bisector** between two points are the same distance from those two points.

Watch out!

Make sure you use the scale given in the question.

---

16 *A*, *B* and *C* are three points on a map.

B
×

A ×

×
C

1 cm represents 100 metres.

Point *T* is 250 metres from point *A*.
Point *T* is equidistant from point *B* and point *C*.

On the map, show one of the possible positions for point *T*.

(Total for Question 16 is 3 marks)

Turn to page 133 for complete worked solutions to the questions on this page.

PROBABILITY AND STATISTICS

 Revision Guide Page 129

7 The table shows the probabilities that a biased dice will land on 2, on 3, on 4, on 5 and on 6.

Number on dice	1	2	3	4	5	6
Probability		0.17	0.18	0.09	0.15	0.1

Neymar rolls the biased dice 200 times.

Work out an estimate for the total number of times the dice will land on 1 or on 3.

....

(Total for Question 17 is 3 marks)

Watch out!

In the context of a probability question involving lots of trials, 'estimate' means 'predict', not 'round'.

LEARN IT!

The **probabilities** of all the different outcomes add up to 1.

Problem solved!

1. Work out the probability of the dice landing on 1.

2. Predict the number of times the dice will land on 1 in 200 trials.

3. Predict the number of times the dice will land on 3 in 200 trials.

4. Add these to predict the number of times the dice will land on 1 **or** 3 in 200 trials.

Watch out!

Read the question carefully – it asks for the **number** of 1s or 3s, not a probability.

NUMBER

Revision Guide
Page 14, 55,
56, 60

Hint

Set out your working
clearly, showing one
step at a time.

LEARN IT!

To convert a fraction
into a percentage
multiply by 100.

Problem solved!

1. Work out the fraction
of children with seats in
the Circle.

2. Work out the total
number of children.

3. Using the ratio, the
total number of children
represents 2 parts, so
work out 1 part.

4. Work out the total
number of adults by
multiplying the value of
1 part by 5.

5. Add the total
number of children and
the total number of
adults.

6. Work out the
percentage of seats
occupied.

7. Compare your
answer with 60%.

8. Answer the question,
saying yes or no.

18 On Saturday, some adults and some children were in a
theatre.
The ratio of the number of adults to the number of
children was 5 : 2

Each person had a seat in the Circle or had a seat in the
Stalls.

$\frac{3}{4}$ of the children had seats in the Stalls.

117 children had seats in the Circle.

There are exactly 2600 seats in the theatre.

On this Saturday, were there people on more than 60% of
the seats?
You must show how you get your answer.

(Total for Question 18 is 5 marks

Turn to page 133 for complete worked solutions to the questions on this page

9 The diagram shows a prism with a cross section in the shape of a trapezium.

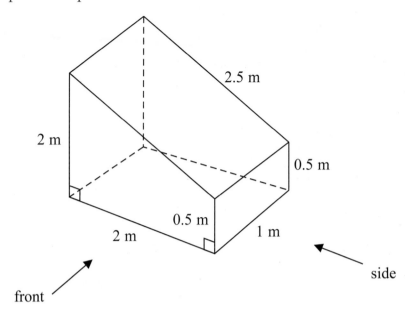

On the centimetre grid below, draw the front elevation and the side elevation of the prism.
Use a scale of 2 cm to 1 m.

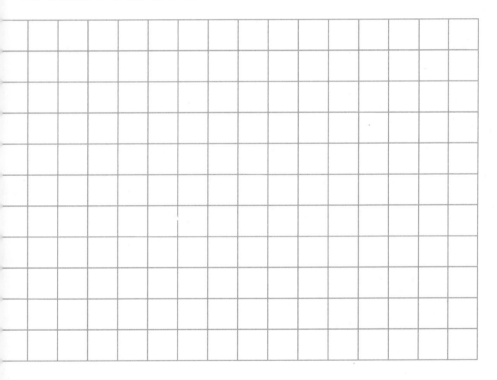

GEOMETRY
AND MEASURES

Revision Guide
Page 97

Hint

Use a ruler and a sharp pencil to draw the two elevations.

Hint

Draw the views of the shape as if you were looking at it directly from the front and then from the side.

Hint

Use the scale given to work out the side lengths of the elevations. The question says that each metre is represented by **two** centimetres on the grid.

Watch out!

Remember to draw a solid line to show the change of depth.

(Total for Question 19 is 4 marks)

urn to page 134 for complete worked solutions to the questions on this page.

% RATIO AND PROPORTION

Revision Guide
Page 64

LEARN IT!

Average speed

$= \dfrac{\text{total distance}}{\text{total time}}$

Hint

Write down the formula for speed and sketch the formula triangle.

Problem solved!

1. Work out the time taken to drive from Liverpool to Manchester.

2. Convert 75 minutes into hours.

3. Work out the total distance from Liverpool to Sheffield.

4. Find the total time taken to drive from Liverpool to Sheffield.

5. Use the formula to work out the average speed.

Hint

You may want to think about the time taken for each journey.

---

20 Olly drove 56 km from Liverpool to Manchester.

He then drove 61 km from Manchester to Sheffield.

Olly's average speed from Liverpool to Manchester was 70 km/h.

Olly took 75 minutes to drive from Manchester to Sheffield.

(a) Work out Olly's average speed for his total drive from Liverpool to Sheffield.

.... km/h

(4)

Janie drove from Barnsley to York.

Janie's average speed from Barnsley to Leeds was 80 km/h.
Her average speed from Leeds to York was 60 km/h.

Janie says that the average speed from Barnsley to York can be found by working out the mean of 80 km/h and 60 km/h.

(b) If Janie is correct, what does this tell you about the two parts of Janie's journey?

....

....

(1)

(Total for Question 20 is 5 marks)

Turn to page 134 for complete worked solutions to the questions on this page.

1

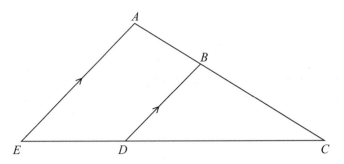

ABC and *EDC* are straight lines.

EA is parallel to *DB*.

EC = 8.1 cm.
DC = 5.4 cm.
DB = 2.6 cm.

(a) Work out the length of *AE*.

.... cm

(2)

AC = 6.15 cm.

(b) Work out the length of *AB*.

.... cm

(2)

(Total for Question 21 is 4 marks)

urn to page 134 for complete worked solutions to the questions on this page.

 GEOMETRY AND MEASURES

Revision Guide
Page 110

Hint

Sketch triangles *ACE* and *BCD* separately and label them. The arrows indicate parallel sides, so triangles *ACE* and *BCD* are similar.

LEARN IT!

Similar triangles have the same angles. The corresponding sides in similar triangles are in the same ratio – they are enlargements of each other.

Hint

Work out $\frac{EC}{DC}$ to find the scale factor.

Hint

Use the scale factor to find the length of *BC* and then use length *BC* to find the length of *AB*.

Revision Guide
Page 63

LEARN IT!

Compound interest
means you earn
interest on the interest
earned previously.

Hint

You will need to write
each increase of 2%,
4.3% and 0.9% as a
multiplier.

To find the multiplier for
a 2% increase:
• 100% + 2% = 102%
• 102% ÷ 100 = 1.02

22 Anil wants to invest £25 000 for 3 years in a bank.

Personal Bank	Secure Bank
Compound Interest	Compound Interest
2% for each year	4.3% for the first year
	0.9% for each extra year

Which bank will give Anil the most interest at the end of
3 years?
You must show all your working.

(Total for Question 22 is 3 marks

 NUMBER

Revision Guide
Pages 3, 32

LEARN IT!

An **error interval** is
written as an inequality
in the form $a \leq x < b$.

23 A number, n, is rounded to 2 decimal places.
The result is 4.76.

Using inequalities, write down the error interval for n.

....

(Total for Question 23 is 2 marks

Turn to page 134 for complete worked solutions to the questions on this page.

24 Solve $x^2 + 5x - 24 = 0$

....

(Total for Question 24 is 3 marks)

$\sqrt{xy^2}$ ALGEBRA

Revision Guide
Pages 46, 47

Problem solved!

1. Find two numbers that add up to 5 and multiply to give -24. One of the numbers is positive and the other one is negative

2. Write your quadratic equation as $(x + \square)(x - \square) = 0$.

3. Set each expression equal to zero and solve both equations.

Watch out!

The quadratic expression has two brackets so make sure you solve both of them.

LEARN IT!

You must know how to multiply positive and negative numbers:

$+ \times + = +$

$- \times - = +$

$- \times + = -$

$+ \times - = -$

 **ALGEBRA**

 Revision Guide
Page 34

Hint

Write the difference
between each term of
the sequence to find
the common difference.
Then subtract the
common difference
from the first term to
work out the zero term.

LEARN IT!

nth term =

$\dfrac{\text{common}}{\text{difference}} \times n + \dfrac{\text{zero}}{\text{term}}$

Hint

Substitute $n = 4$ into
$3n^2$ and evaluate it. Do
you get 144?

Hint

Make sure you show
enough working and
that you answer the
question.

25 Here are the first six terms of an arithmetic sequence.

$$3 \quad 8 \quad 13 \quad 18 \quad 23 \quad 28$$

(a) Find an expression, in terms of n, for the nth term of
     this sequence.

....

(2

The nth term of a different sequence is $3n^2$
Nathan says that the 4th term of this sequence is 144.

(b) Is Nathan right?
     Show how you get your answer.

(1

(Total for Question 25 is 3 marks

TOTAL FOR PAPER 2F IS 80 MARKS

Turn to page 135 for complete worked solutions to the questions on this page.

Paper 3F: Calculator
Time allowed: 1 hour 30 minutes

The table shows the lengths of five rivers.

River	Length (km)
Trent	297
Don	112
Severn	354
Thames	346
Mersey	113

(a) Write down the rivers in order of length.

Start with the shortest river.

....

....

(1)

Ami says,

"The River Thames is more than three times as long as the River Don."

(b) Show that Ami is correct.

....

....

(1)

(Total for Question 1 is 2 marks)

$\sqrt{xy^2}$ **ALGEBRA**

 Revision Guide
Page 27

Problem solved!

Plan your strategy:
- multiply the number of cups in each pack by the number of packs
- multiply the number of cups in each box by the number of boxes
- add them to give an expression for the total.

LEARN IT!

Do not leave multiplication signs in algebraic terms. Write e.g. $2 \times x$ as $2x$.

^{1}**2**^{3} **NUMBER**

 Revision Guide
Page 1

Hint

Look for the two smallest digits.

Hint

Choose three digits. Make numbers close to 200 and work out which is closest.

---

2 Cups are sold in packs and in boxes.

There are 12 cups in each pack.
There are 18 cups in each box.

Alison buys p packs of cups and b boxes of cups.

Write down an expression, in terms of p and b, for the total number of cups Alison buys.

....

(Total for Question 2 is 2 marks

---

3 Here are four digits.

$$5 \qquad 6 \qquad 1 \qquad 9$$

(i) Write down the smallest possible two digit number that can be made with two of the digits.

....
(1

(ii) Write down the three digit number closest to 200 that can be made with three of the digits.

....
(1

(Total for Question 3 is 2 marks

 Turn to page 136 for complete worked solutions to the questions on this page.

$\frac{4}{5}$ of a number is 32

Find the number.

....

(Total for Question 4 is 2 marks)

A path is made of white tiles and grey tiles.

$\frac{1}{4}$ of the tiles are white.

(a) Write down the ratio of white tiles to grey tiles.

....

(1)

There is a total of 56 tiles.

(b) Work out the number of grey tiles.

....

(2)

(Total for Question 5 is 3 marks)

urn to page 136 for complete worked solutions to the questions on this page.

 NUMBER

 Revision Guide
Page 13

Hint

$\frac{4}{5}$ represents 32 so work out what a whole one, i.e. $\frac{5}{5}$ represents.

Watch out!

$\frac{4}{5}$ represents 32 so your final answer must be greater than 32.

% RATIO AND PROPORTION

Revision Guide
Page 59

Hint

The denominator (the number beneath the line in a fraction) tells you the total number of parts.

Hint

The numerator (the number above the line in a fraction) tells you the number of parts for the white tiles.

Watch out!

The ratio is not $1:4$.

PROBABILITY AND STATISTICS

 Revision Guide
Page 120

LEARN IT!

To find the **median** write the numbers from the smallest to the largest. The median is the value in the middle.

LEARN IT!

Range = highest − lowest
number   number

Hint

Add up all the values.

LEARN IT!

Mean =

$$\frac{\text{sum of all values}}{\text{total number of values}}$$

Watch out!

Check your answer. Does it look about right, given the numbers in the list?

---

6   Here is a list of numbers.

12   15   14   17   22   19   13

Bridgit says,

"To work out the median you find the middle number, so the median of these numbers is 17"

Bridgit's answer is **not** correct.

(a) What is wrong with Bridgit's method?

....

....

(1

(b) Work out the range of the numbers in the list.

....

(2

(c) Work out the mean of the numbers in the list.

....

(2

(Total for Question 6 is 5 marks

Turn to page 136 for complete worked solutions to the questions on this page.

Priti is going to have a meal.

She can choose one starter and one main course from the menu.

Menu	
Starter	**Main Course**
Salad	Pasta
Fish	Rice
Melon	Burger

Write down all the possible combinations Priti can choose.

....

....

....

(Total for Question 7 is 2 marks)

Joanne wants to buy a dishwasher.

The dishwasher costs £372

Joanne will pay a deposit of £36
She will then pay the rest of the cost in 4 equal monthly payments.

How much is each monthly payment?

£ ....

(Total for Question 8 is 2 marks)

rn to page 137 for complete worked solutions to the questions on this page.

GEOMETRY AND MEASURES

 Revision Guide
Page 77

Hint

You will need to convert all the times given into minutes.

LEARN IT!

1 hour = 60 minutes

Problem solved!

1. Add up all the minutes, for time working and for break time.

2. Convert into hours and minutes.

3. Add the total number of hours and minutes to 9 am.

9 Davos is a cleaner.

The table shows information about the time it will take him to clean each of four rooms in a house.

Room	Time
Kitchen	2 hours
Sitting room	1 hour 40 minutes
Bedroom	$1\frac{1}{2}$ hours
Bathroom	45 minutes

Davos wants to clean all four rooms in one day.

He will have breaks for a total time of 75 minutes.

Davos is going to start cleaning at 9 am.

Will he finish cleaning by 4 pm?

You must show all your working.

(Total for Question 9 is 3 mark

Turn to page 137 for complete worked solutions to the questions on this page

ABC is a straight line.

A   B   C

The length AB is five times the length BC.
AC = 90 cm.

Work out the length AB.

% **RATIO AND PROPORTION**

Revision Guide
Page 60

Problem solved!

Plan your strategy:
- write the lengths of AB : BC as a ratio
- use the ratio to find the total number of parts
- work out the value of 1 part
- multiply this by the number of parts represented by AB.

.... cm

(Total for Question 10 is 3 marks)

$T = 4v + 3$

(a) Work out the value of T when $v = 2$

$4 \times 2 = 8 + 3 = 11$

$T = ..11..........................$

(2)

(b) Make v the subject of the formula $T = 4v + 3$

$ -3 -3$

$t =$

$t - 3 = 4v$

$v = \dfrac{t - 3}{4}$

....

(2)

(Total for Question 11 is 4 marks)

√xy² **ALGEBRA**

Revision Guide
Pages 25, 50

Hint

Substitute $v = 2$ into the formula and evaluate for T.

Watch out!

$4v$ means $4 \times v$.

Hint

To make v the subject you need to get v on its own on one side of the equals sign, so the formula starts $v = ...$.

rn to page 137 for complete worked solutions to the questions on this page.

GEOMETRY AND MEASURES

 Revision Guide Page 83

12 The diagram shows a cube of side length 2 cm.

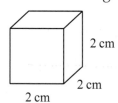

2 cm

2 cm

2 cm

Vera says,

"The volume of any solid made with 6 of these cubes is 48 cm³"

(a) Is Vera correct?
You must show your working.

....

....

....

(

Hint

You need to find the volume of 6 cubes.

(b) (i) Draw a cuboid that can be made with 6 of these cubes.
Write the dimensions of the cuboid on your diagram.

LEARN IT!

Volume of cuboid =
length × width × height

Explore

There is more than one way to use 6 cubes to make a cuboid. Try finding other ways.

Hint

This question is about surface area. Surface area is the total area of the faces of a 3D shape.

(ii) Work out the surface area of your cuboid.

LEARN IT!

Area of rectangle
= length × width

.... cm

(

Watch out!

Make sure you work out the surface area of all 6 faces.

(Total for Question 12 is 5 mark

Turn to page 137 for complete worked solutions to the questions on this page

The size of the largest angle in a triangle is 4 times the size of the smallest angle.
The other angle is 27° less than the largest angle.

Work out, in degrees, the size of each angle in the triangle.
You must show your working.

Problem solved!

Plan your strategy:
- let x represent the smallest angle
- write down the other two angles in terms of x
- write down an expression for the sum of the angles in terms of x and make it equal to 180°
- solve the equation for x
- use your value for x to work out the other two angles.

Hint

Check that your angles add to 180°.

LEARN IT!

Angles in a triangle add up to 180°.

..................°, ...°, ...°

(Total for Question 13 is 5 marks)

RATIO AND PROPORTION

 Revision Guide
Page 67

Watch out!

Make sure you apply the conversion rate correctly. \$1.90 = £1, so to convert from dollars to pounds you need to divide.

Problem solved!

1. Work out the total cost of the hotel in dollars.

2. Work out the total cost of the wifi in dollars.

3. Add the cost of the hotel and wifi and convert this total to pounds.

4. Add the cost of flights and the cost of the hotel and wifi to find the total cost.

Hint

Try dividing your cost in dollars by a lower value than 1.90.

---

14 Andy went on holiday to Canada.
His flights cost a total of £1500

Andy stayed for 14 nights.
His hotel room cost \$196 per night.

Andy used wifi for 12 days.
Wifi cost \$5 per day.

The exchange rate was \$1.90 to £1

(a) Work out the total cost of the flights, the hotel room and wifi. Give your answer in pounds.

£ ....

(b) If there were fewer dollars to £1, what effect would this have on the total cost, in pounds, of Andy's holiday?

....

(Total for Question 14 is 6 mark

Turn to page 138 for complete worked solutions to the questions on this pag

PROBABILITY AND STATISTICS

Revision Guide
Pages 127, 131

5 $\mathscr{E}$ = {odd numbers less than 30}

$A = \{3, 9, 15, 21, 27\}$

$B = \{5, 15, 25\}$

(a) Complete the Venn diagram to represent this information.

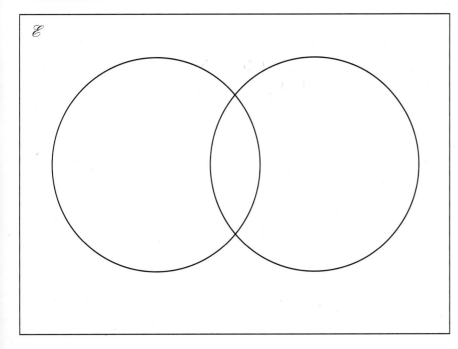

(4)

A number is chosen at random from the universal set, $\mathscr{E}$.

(b) What is the probability that the number is in the set $A \cup B$?

....

(2)

(Total for Question 15 is 6 marks)

Turn to page 138 for complete worked solutions to the questions on this page.

Problem solved!

1. Write all the numbers in the universal set ($\mathscr{E}$) in a list.

2. Label sets A and B on the diagram.

3. Write the numbers in the different sections starting with the intersection (overlap) between A and B.

4. Write the numbers in sets A and B.

5. Write any remaining numbers outside A and B.

Watch out!

No number should appear more than once in the Venn diagram.

Hint

$A \cup B$ means A **or** B **or** both; it is represented by the shaded area in this Venn diagram.

LEARN IT!

Probability =

$$\frac{\text{number of successful outcomes}}{\text{total number of possible outcomes}}$$

ALGEBRA

Revision Guide
Page 49

Hint

It helps to number your equations to show what you are doing at different steps.

Hint

Look for coefficients of x or y that are the same in the two equations.

Problem solved!

Plan your strategy:
- choose a variable (x or y) to eliminate
- if the coefficient of your chosen variable is the same in both equations, simply add or subtract to eliminate the variable
- solve the resulting equation
- use the solution to work out the value of the other variable.

LEARN IT!

Coefficient is the word used to describe a number in front of x or y.

---

16 Solve the simultaneous equations

$$3x + y = -4$$
$$3x - 4y = 6$$

$$5y = -10$$
$$\div 5 \qquad \div 5$$
$$y = -5$$

$$-15 + y = -4$$
$$+15 \qquad +15$$
$$y = 11$$

$$y = -2$$

$$-6 - 4y = 6$$
$$+6 \qquad +6$$
$$-4y = 12$$
$$\div -4 \quad \div -4$$

$$-6 +$$
$$3x + 8$$

$$3x1$$

$$3x - 2y = -4$$
$$-3 \qquad -3$$
$$-2y = -7$$

$$-\frac{7}{2}$$

$x = $ ....

$y = $ ....

(Total for Question 16 is 3 mark

Turn to page 138 for complete worked solutions to the questions on this page

The table shows some information about the dress sizes of 25 women.

Dress size	Number of women
8	2
10	9
12	8
14	6

(a) Find the median dress size.

....
(1)

3 of the 25 women have a shoe size of 7

Zoe says that if you choose at random one of the 25 women, the probability that she has either a shoe size of 7 or a dress size of 14 is $\frac{9}{25}$ because

$$\frac{3}{25} + \frac{6}{25} = \frac{9}{25}$$

(b) Is Zoe correct?

You must give a reason for your answer.

....

....
(1)

(Total for Question 17 is 2 marks)

 PROBABILITY AND STATISTICS

Revision Guide
Page 121

Hint

Write down the **cumulative frequency** on the side of the table.

LEARN IT!

The **median** is the middle value in a data set. For n data values, the median = $\frac{1}{2}(n + 1)$th value.

Hint

Use your cumulative frequency to work out which class interval contains the median (13th) data value.

Hint

Can the event 'shoe size of 7' and the event 'dress size of 14' happen at the same time?

LEARN IT!

Events are **mutually exclusive** when they **cannot** happen at the same time.

urn to page 139 for complete worked solutions to the questions on this page.

RATIO AND PROPORTION

 Revision Guide
Page 56, 60

Hint

Read the question carefully. Use your calculator but set your work out in a clear, methodical way, writing down all your steps.

Problem solved!

Plan your strategy:

- work out $\frac{2}{7}$ of 420
- work out 35% of 420
- subtract these two values from 420 to find the number of lemon cakes and chocolate cakes
- use the ratio of lemon cakes and chocolate cakes to work out the total number of parts
- work out 1 part
- multiply this by the number of parts for the lemon cakes.

Watch out!

Make sure you read the ratio correctly as the lemon cakes come first.

---

18 Daniel bakes 420 cakes.

He bakes only vanilla cakes, banana cakes, lemon cakes and chocolate cakes.

$\frac{2}{7}$ of the cakes are vanilla cakes.

35% of the cakes are banana cakes.

The ratio of the number of lemon cakes to the number of chocolate cakes is $4:5$

Work out the number of lemon cakes Daniel bakes.

....

(Total for Question 18 is 5 marks

Turn to page 139 for complete worked solutions to the questions on this page

In the diagram, *AB*, *BC* and *CD* are three sides of a regular polygon **P**.

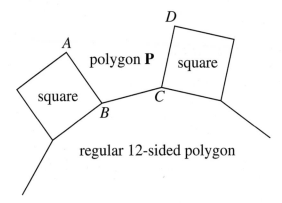

Show that polygon **P** is a hexagon.
You must show your working.

GEOMETRY AND MEASURES

Revision Guide Page 76

Hint

You need to work out angle *DCB*.

LEARN IT!

- Exterior angle of regular polygon
$$= \frac{360}{\text{number of sides}}$$
- Angles on a straight line add up to 180°.
- Angles around a point add up to 360°.
- In a regular polygon all the sides are equal and all the angles are equal.

Explore

A 12-sided shape is called a dodecagon. A polygon with a million sides is called a megagon and one with a google (10^{100}) sides is a called a googolgon.

(Total for Question 19 is 4 marks)

Turn to page 139 for complete worked solutions to the questions on this page.

Revision Guide
Page 65

Hint

Write down the formula for density, mass and volume. Sketch a formula triangle to help.

LEARN IT!

Density $= \dfrac{\text{mass}}{\text{volume}}$

Problem solved!

Plan your strategy:
- use the formula to work out the mass of the apple juice, the fruit syrup and the carbonated water
- work out the total mass of the drink
- use the formula to work out the density of the combined drink.

Watch out!

Round your answer to 2 decimal places as specified in the question.

20 The density of apple juice is 1.05 grams per cm^3.

The density of fruit syrup is 1.4 grams per cm^3.

The density of carbonated water is 0.99 grams per cm^3.

25 cm^3 of apple juice are mixed with 15 cm^3 of fruit syrup and 280 cm^3 of carbonated water to make a drink with a volume of 320 cm^3.

Work out the density of the drink.
Give your answer correct to 2 decimal places.

.... g/cr

(Total for Question 20 is 4 mark

Turn to page 139 for complete worked solutions to the questions on this page

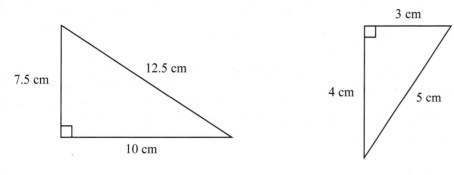

Show that these two triangles are mathematically similar.

(Total for Question 21 is 2 marks)

GEOMETRY AND MEASURES

Revision Guide Page 110

Hint

Match up pairs of corresponding sides. Then work out the scale factor for each pair of sides.

LEARN IT!

Shapes are mathematically **similar** if corresponding pairs of sides have the same scale factor.

Hint

Scale factor =
$$\frac{\text{side of one triangle}}{\text{corresponding side of other triangle}}$$

Explore

Does it make any difference if you work out the scale factor by going from the large triangle to the small triangle instead of from the small to the large?

√xy² **ALGEBRA**

Revision Guide
Page 48

Hint

To complete the table,
substitute each value
of x into the right-
hand side of the
equation and work out
the corresponding
value of y.

Hint

The graph should be a
curve. If any point does
not follow the pattern,
check your working.

Watch out!

Read the scales on
the axes carefully,
especially when
plotting decimal values.

Watch out!

Join the plotted points
with a **smooth curve**,
not with straight lines.

 **Explore**

A **reciprocal graph**
gets closer and closer
to the x-axis and
the y-axis but never
touches them.

22 (a) Complete the table of values for $y = \dfrac{6}{x}$

x	0.5	1	1.5	2	3	4	5	6
y		6		3		1.5		

(

(b) On the grid below, draw the graph of $y = \dfrac{6}{x}$ for values
of x from 0.5 to 6

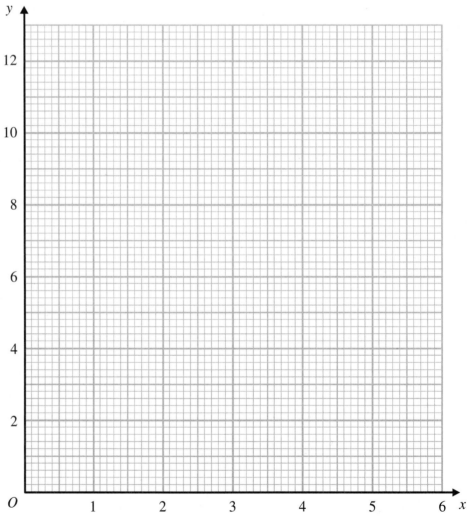

(

(Total for Question 22 is 4 mark

Turn to page 140 for complete worked solutions to the questions on this page

3 Harley's house has a value of £160 000 correct to 2 significant figures.

(a) (i) Write down the least possible value of the house.

£ ....
(1)

(ii) Write down the greatest possible value of the house.

£ ....
(1)

The value of Rita's house increased by 5%.
Her house then had a value of £210 000

(b) Work out the value of Rita's house before the increase.

£ ....
(2)

(Total for Question 23 is 4 marks)

TOTAL FOR PAPER 3F IS 80 MARKS

NUMBER

RATIO AND PROPORTION

Revision Guide Page 3, 62

Hint

160 000 is correct to 2 significant figures. So the exact value lies in a range from half a unit (10 000 ÷ 2) above to half a unit below the given number.

Hint

This is a **reverse percentage** question. You need to work out the cost before the 5% increase.

Hint

Add 5% to 100%. Let 105% represent 210 000, find 1% and then find 100%.

Watch out!

The house has increased in value so your final answer should be less than £210 000.

Revision Guide
Page 61

Hint

To change cm into metres, divide by the conversion factor.

LEARN IT!

$1\,m = 100\,cm$

Hint

To change kg into g, multiply by the conversion factor.

LEARN IT!

$1\,kg = 1000\,g$

 **NUMBER**

 Revision Guide
Page 8

Hint

Use **BIDMAS** (**B**rackets, **I**ndices, **D**ivide, **M**ultiply, **A**dd, **S**ubtract) to apply the correct priority (order) of operations. Multiply before adding.

Paper 1: Non-calculator
Time allowed: 1 hour 30 minutes

1 (a) Change 365 cm into metres.

....

(b) Change 2.7 kg into grams.

....

(Total for Question 1 is 2 marks)

---

2 Work out $2 + 7 \times 10$

....

(Total for Question 2 is 1 mark)

Turn to page 141 for complete worked solutions to the questions on this page

Solve $\dfrac{y}{4} = 10.5$

$y =$ ....

(Total for Question 3 is 1 mark)

Here are four numbers.

$$-9 \quad -2 \quad 2 \quad 9$$

Write one of these numbers in each box to make a correct calculation.

$$\boxed{} + \boxed{} = -7$$

(Total for Question 4 is 1 mark)

$\sqrt{xy^2}$ **ALGEBRA**

Revision Guide
Page 30

Problem solved!

To solve an equation you need to get the letter on its own on one side of the equals sign. To do this here you multiply both sides by 4.

123 NUMBER

Revision Guide
Page 2

Hint

The final answer is negative so think about which number is negative and which number is positive.

Explore

If you add two numbers in a different order, does this affect the answer?

urn to page 141 for complete worked solutions to the questions on this page.

 Revision Guide
Page 34

Hint

You must always follow the rule given, so here you must multiply first and then add 1. Show all the steps of your working.

 Revision Guide
Page 27

Problem solved!

Plan your strategy:
- write down the lengths of the 5 rods
- set up a formula by writing L = sum of the five rods
- simplify your answer.

Hint

Simplify your expression by collecting all the a terms together and all the number terms together.

---

5 Here are the first four terms of a number sequence.

$$2 \qquad 5 \qquad 11 \qquad 23$$

The rule to continue this sequence is

multiply the previous term by 2 and then add 1

Work out the 5th term of this sequence.

....

(Total for Question 5 is 1 mark)

---

6 Here are five straight rods.

<── $a-1$ ──> <── a ──> <── a ──> <── a ──> <─────── $a+4$ ───────>

All measurements are in centimetres.

The total length of the five rods is L cm.

Find a formula for L in terms of a.
Write your formula as simply as possible.

....

(Total for Question 6 is 3 marks)

Turn to page 141 for complete worked solutions to the questions on this page

√xy² **ALGEBRA**

Revision Guide
Pages 36, 38

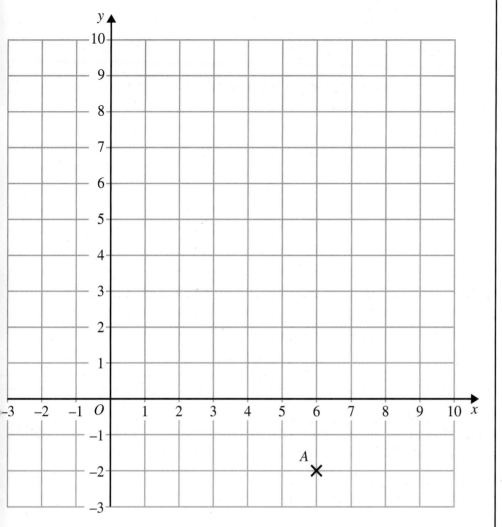

(a) Write down the coordinates of the point *A*.

LEARN IT!

Always write
coordinates as (*x*, *y*).

(................................. , ...)

(1)

Hint

You need to go 2 units across and then 9 units up. Use a cross (✗) to plot the point.

Hint

Substitute the values of *x* and *y* into the given equation.

Hint

Use a ruler to draw a straight line.

GEOMETRY AND MEASURES

 Revision Guide Page 79

Hint

Write down all the possible multiplications that give 32.

Watch out!

Don't mix up the area and the perimeter of a rectangle. The **area** is the space inside and the **perimeter** is the distance around the edge.

(b) (i) Plot the point with coordinates (2, 9).
Label this point *B*.

(

(ii) Does point *B* lie on the straight line with equation
$y = 4x + 1$?
You must show how you get your answer.

....

(

(c) On the grid, draw the line with equation $x = -2$

(

(Total for Question 7 is 4 mark

8 The length of a rectangle is twice as long as the width of the rectangle.
The area of the rectangle is 32 cm².

Draw the rectangle on the centimetre grid.

(Total for Question 8 is 2 mark

Turn to page 142 for complete worked solutions to the questions on this page

Jacqui wants to work out   3480 ÷ 5

She knows that   3480 ÷ 10 = 348

Jacqui writes   3480 ÷ 5 = 174

because   10 ÷ 5 = 2

and   348 ÷ 2 = 174

What mistake did Jacqui make in her method?

....

....

(Total for Question 9 is 1 mark)

rn to page 142 for complete worked solutions to the questions on this page.

¹₂³ NUMBER

Revision Guide
Page 5

Hint

Read through Jacqui's
method carefully. Then
write down the steps
as if you are working
out the problem.

Watch out!

Check whether the
answer makes sense.
If 3480 ÷ 10 = 348,
then 3480 ÷ 5 must
be bigger than 348
because you are
dividing by a smaller
number.

Revision Guide
Page 124

10 Jake and Sarah each played a computer game six times.

Their scores for each game are shown below.

Jake	10	9	8	11	12	8
Sarah	2	10	7	14	4	10

(a) Who had the most consistent scores, Jake or Sarah?
You must give a reason for your answer.

....

Jake played a different game 20 times.

The stem and leaf diagram shows information about his scores.

0	9
1	2 3 3 4 5
2	5 6 6 6 6 7
3	1 3 4 6 8
4	0 2 9

Key
1 | 2 represents 12 points

Jake said his modal score was 6 points because 6 occurs most often in the diagram.

(b) Is Jake correct?
You must explain your answer.

....

....

(Total for Question 10 is 2 mark

Turn to page 142 for complete worked solutions to the questions on this pag

There are 30 children in a nursery school.
At least 1 adult is needed for every 8 children in the nursery.

(a) Work out the least number of adults needed in the nursery.

....

(2)

2 more children join the nursery.

(b) Does this mean that more adults are needed in the nursery? You must give a reason for your answer.

....

(1)

(Total for Question 11 is 3 marks)

Emma has 45 rabbits.

30 of the rabbits are male.
8 of the female rabbits have short hair.
12 of the rabbits with long hair are male.

(a) Use the information to complete the two-way table.

	Male	Female	Total
Long hair			
Short hair			
Total			

(3)

rn to page 142 for complete worked solutions to the questions on this page.

---

¹₂³ NUMBER

Revision Guide
Pages 4, 5

Hint

Count up in 8s until you get a number greater than 30.

Hint

Work out the total number of children and then divide by 8.

PROBABILITY AND STATISTICS

Revision Guide
Pages 115, 127

Hint

There are 45 rabbits in total so write 45 in the bottom right-hand corner. Then write each piece of information into the correct cell in the table. Use addition or subtraction to find the missing entries.

Watch out!

Make sure both the row and the column totals add up to 45.

One of Emma's rabbits is chosen at random.

(b) Write down the probability that this rabbit is a female with short hair.

....

(

(Total for Question 12 is 4 marks

---

13 The total surface area of a cube is 294 cm².

Work out the volume of the cube.

.... cm

(Total for Question 13 is 4 marks

Turn to page 143 for complete worked solutions to the questions on this page

14 Here are two fractions.

$$\frac{7}{5} \qquad \frac{5}{7}$$

Work out which of the fractions is closer to 1
You must show all your working.

(Total for Question 14 is 3 marks)

 NUMBER

Revision Guide
Page 13

Hint

Write both fractions
and 1 as equivalent
fractions with a
common denominator.
Then use subtraction to
work out the difference
between each fraction
and 1.

15 There are only red buttons, yellow buttons and orange
buttons in a jar.
The number of red buttons, the number of yellow buttons
and the number of orange buttons are in the ratio 7 : 4 : 9

Work out what percentage of the buttons in the jar are
orange.

.... %

(Total for Question 15 is 2 marks)

 RATIO AND PROPORTION

Revision Guide
Page 55

Problem solved!

1. Add all the ratio
parts to find the total
number of parts.

2. Write the number of
parts that are orange
as a fraction of the
total number of parts.

3. Multiply by 100 to
find the percentage of
orange buttons.

urn to page 143 for complete worked solutions to the questions on this page.

% RATIO AND PROPORTION

Revision Guide
Pages 10, 58

Hint

Berenika has rounded up both values.

LEARN IT!

When rounding **up** values, the answer is an **overestimate**. When rounding **down** values, the answer is an **underestimate**.

Watch out!

This is a non-calculator paper. Use written methods for all your calculations – take care to avoid making simple errors.

Problem solved!

Plan your strategy:
- work out the cost of 35 T-shirts
- work out 10% of the total cost of 35 T-shirts
- subtract 10% from the total cost of the 35 T-shirts.

16 Berenika wants to buy 35 T-shirts.

Each T-shirt costs £5.80
Berenika does the calculation $40 \times 6 = 240$ to estimate the cost of 35 T-shirts.

(a) Explain how Berenika's calculation shows the actual cost will be less than £240

....

....

....

(1

There is a special offer.

> T-shirts £5.80 each.
>
> Buy 30 or more T-shirts.
> Get 10% off the total cost.

(b) Work out the actual cost of buying 35 T-shirts using the special offer.

£ ....

(4

(Total for Question 16 is 5 marks

Turn to page 143 for complete worked solutions to the questions on this page.

17 There are 3 cards in Box **A** and 3 cards in Box **B**.
There is a number on each card.

Box **A**

Box **B**

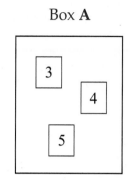

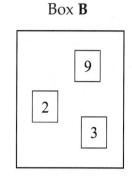

Ryan takes at random a card from Box **A** and a card from Box **B**.

He adds together the numbers on the two cards to get a total score.

Work out the probability that the total score is an odd number.

PROBABILITY AND STATISTICS

Revision Guide
Pages 127, 128

Hint

Work out all the different total scores by systematically writing out all the possible combinations: for example,
3 + 9 = ...,
3 + 2 = ..., and so on.
Then identify the odd total scores.

LEARN IT!

Probability =

$$\frac{\text{number of successful outcomes}}{\text{total number of possible outcomes}}$$

....

(Total for Question 17 is 2 marks)

urn to page 143 for complete worked solutions to the questions on this page.

73

% RATIO AND PROPORTION

Revision Guide
Pages 59, 60

Problem solved!

1. Work out the total number of parts.

2. Divide the quantity by the total number of parts to find one part.

3. Multiply your answer by each part of the ratio.

% RATIO AND PROPORTION

Revision Guide
Page 67

Problem solved!

Using 24 = 8 + 16, work out the amount of each ingredient needed for 8 flapjacks and add to the amount needed for 16 flapjacks.

---

18 Harry, Regan and Kelan share £450 in the ratio 2 : 5 : 3

How much money does Kelan get?

£ ....

(Total for Question 18 is 2 marks

---

19 Here is a list of ingredients for making 16 flapjacks.

Ingredients for 16 flapjacks
120 g butter
140 g brown sugar
250 g oats
2 tablespoons syrup

Jenny wants to make 24 flapjacks.

Work out how much of each of the ingredients she needs.

butter ....

brown sugar ....

oats ....

syrup .... tablespoon

(Total for Question 19 is 3 marks

Turn to page 144 for complete worked solutions to the questions on this page.

20 Ami and Josh use a calculator to work out $\dfrac{595}{4.08^2 + 5.3}$

Ami's answer is 27.1115
Josh's answer is 271.115

One of these answers is correct.

Use approximations to find out which answer is correct.

(Total for Question 20 is 3 marks)

 NUMBER

Revision Guide
Page 10

Hint

Round each number to
1 significant figure to
find an approximation.

Watch out!

Do not simply write Ami
or Josh. You must show
how you arrive at your
conclusion.

21 Work out $\dfrac{0.06 \times 0.0003}{0.01}$

Give your answer in standard form.

....

(Total for Question 21 is 3 marks)

 NUMBER

Revision Guide
Page 18

Hint

Write each number in
standard form. Then
use the **laws of indices**
(powers) to simplify the
fraction.

LEARN IT!

$a^m \times a^n = a^{m+n}$ and
$a^m \div a^n = a^{m-n}$

LEARN IT!

A number written in
standard form is in the
form $n \times 10^x$ where
$n \leq 1$ and x is an
integer (whole number).

NUMBER

Revision Guide
Pages 9, 14

LEARN IT!

$a^{-n} = \dfrac{1}{a^n}$

 **NUMBER**

Revision Guide
Page 11

Problem solved!

You can use a factor
tree to find prime
factors:

- choose a factor pair
  of the number
- for each factor, keep
  finding factor pairs
- circle the prime
  factors as you
  go along
- continue until each
  branch ends with a
  prime number.

 **LEARN IT!**

A **factor pair** of
a number multiply
together to make
the number.

22 (a) Work out $\dfrac{2}{5} + \dfrac{1}{4}$

....

(2

(b) Write down the value of 2^{-3}

....

(1

(Total for Question 22 is 3 marks

23 Write 36 as a product of its prime factors.

....

(Total for Question 23 is 2 marks

Turn to page 144 for complete worked solutions to the questions on this page.

24 Kiaria is 7 years older than Jay.
Martha is twice as old as Kiaria.
The sum of their three ages is 77

Find the ratio of Jay's age to Kiaria's age to Martha's age.

....

(Total for Question 24 is 4 marks)

 Revision Guide
Page 51

Problem solved!

Plan your strategy:
- use a letter such as x to represent one person's age
- write the other ages as expressions in terms of x
- add the expressions and make them equal to the total age
- solve for x
- find each person's age by substituting the value of x into each expression.

Hint

Check your answer by adding the three ages – they should total 77.

Hint

You only need to simplify a ratio if the question instructs you to.

Watch out!

Make sure you write the ages in the order stated in the question.

GEOMETRY
AND MEASURES

Revision Guide
Pages 73, 74,
75

Problem solved!

In angle problems
look out for parallel
lines (marked with
arrows) which create
corresponding,
alternate or co-interior
(allied) angles.

Hint

As you work out each
angle, write it on the
diagram. This helps you
work out which angle
to find next.

LEARN IT!

You need to know the
properties of angles:
• Corresponding
  angles are equal.
• Alternate angles
  are equal.
• Opposite angles in
  a parallelogram are
  equal.
• Sum of angles in a
  triangle = 180°.
• Sum of angles on a
  straight line = 180°.
• Vertically opposite
  angles are equal.
• Sum of angles in a
  quadrilateral = 360°.
• Co-interior (allied)
  angles = 180°.
• Sum of angles around
  a point = 360°.

25

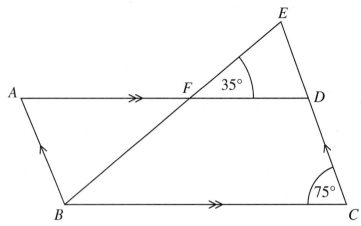

ABCD is a parallelogram.
EDC is a straight line.
F is the point on *AD* so that *BFE* is a straight line.

Angle *EFD* = 35°
Angle *DCB* = 75°

Show that angle *ABF* = 70°
Give a reason for each stage of your working.

(Total for Question 25 is 4 marks

Turn to page 145 for complete worked solutions to the questions on this page.

26 The diagram shows a logo made from three circles.

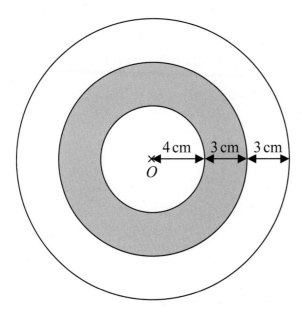

Each circle has centre O.

Daisy says that exactly $\frac{1}{3}$ of the logo is shaded.

Is Daisy correct?
You must show all your working.

(Total for Question 26 is 4 marks)

 GEOMETRY AND MEASURES

 Revision Guide Page 104

Problem solved!

Plan your strategy:
- work out the area of each circle
- work out the shaded area by subtracting the area of the small circle from the area of the middle circle
- work out the shaded area as a proportion of the area of the large circle.

LEARN IT!

Area of a circle = πr^2

Watch out!

Remember to answer the question by saying whether Daisy is correct or incorrect.

Explore

Circles with the same centre and different radii and are called **concentric**. You can see concentric circles in nature, for example: tree rings, the iris of an eye, the rings of Saturn or when a pebble is thrown into a pond.

PROBABILITY
AND STATISTICS

 Revision Guide
Page 122

Hint

You need to find the **midpoint** of each class interval and then multiply it by the frequency.

LEARN IT!

Estimate of mean =

$$\frac{\text{total of (frequency} \times \text{midpoint)}}{\text{total frequency}}$$

Hint

You need to think about outliers.

LEARN IT!

An **outlier** is a value that does not fit the pattern of the given data.

Watch out!

You cannot simply answer yes or no, because the question says you must **justify** your answer.

27 The table shows information about the weekly earnings of 20 people who work in a shop.

Weekly earnings (£x)	Frequency
$150 < x \leqslant 250$	1
$250 < x \leqslant 350$	11
$350 < x \leqslant 450$	5
$450 < x \leqslant 550$	0
$550 < x \leqslant 650$	3

(a) Work out an estimate for the mean of the weekly earnings.

£ ....

(3

Nadiya says,

"The mean may **not** be the best average to use to represent this information."

(b) Do you agree with Nadiya?
You must justify your answer.

....

....

(1

(Total for Question 27 is 4 marks

Turn to page 145 for complete worked solutions to the questions on this page.

8 Here is a rectangle.

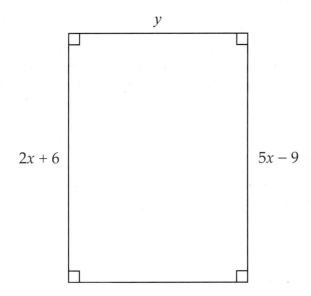

All measurements are in centimetres.

The area of the rectangle is $48\,\text{cm}^2$.

Show that $y = 3$

GEOMETRY AND MEASURES

 Revision Guide Pages 51, 81

Hint

The opposite sides of a rectangle are equal.

Problem solved!

Plan your strategy:
- set up an equation to find the value of x by equating opposite sides
- solve the equation for x
- use the value of x to find the length of the rectangle
- use the formula for the area of a rectangle to work out the value of y.

LEARN IT!

Area of rectangle = length × width

(Total for Question 28 is 4 marks)

urn to page 145 for complete worked solutions to the questions on this page.

Revision Guide
Page 44

29 Brogan needs to draw the graph of $y = x^2 + 1$

Here is her graph.

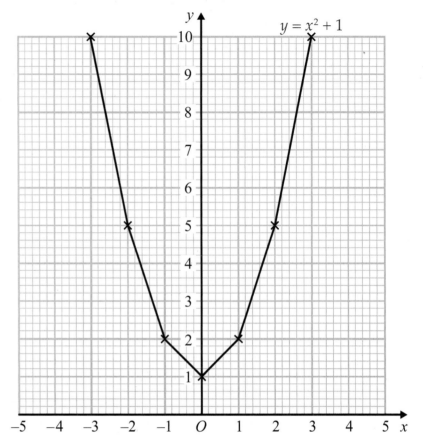

Write down one thing that is wrong with Brogan's graph.

....

....

(Total for Question 29 is 1 mark

Hint

Think about what the **shape** of a quadratic graph should look like.

Turn to page 146 for complete worked solutions to the questions on this page

0 In a sale, the normal price of a book is reduced by 30%.
The sale price of the book is £2.80

Work out the normal price of the book.

£ ....

(Total for Question 30 is 2 marks)

TOTAL FOR PAPER 1F IS 80 MARKS

urn to page 146 for complete worked solutions to the questions on this page.

% RATIO AND PROPORTION

Revision Guide
Page 62

Hint

The price has been **reduced**, so the original price must be greater than the sale price.

Hint

First work out the reduced price as a percentage of 100% (the original price). Use this to find 10% and then 100%.

LEARN IT!

Percentage remaining = 100% − percentage reduction

Watch out!

Do not find 30% of £2.80 and then add this value to £2.80.

RATIO AND PROPORTION

Revision Guide
Page 56

Hint

When you divide by 100 the digits move two places to the right on a place value diagram.

NUMBER

Revision Guide
Page 11

Hint

The multiples of 6 are the numbers in the 6 times table. Write down the numbers in the 6 times table between 40 and 50.

Paper 2: Calculator
Time allowed: 1 hour 30 minutes

1 Write $\dfrac{7}{100}$ as a decimal.

....

(Total for Question 1 is 1 mark)

2 Write down a multiple of 6 that is between 40 and 50

....

(Total for Question 2 is 1 mark)

Turn to page 147 for complete worked solutions to the questions on this page.

(a) Simplify $3f \times 5g$

....

(1)

(b) Simplify $t \times t$

....

(1)

(c) Simplify $\dfrac{2n + 6n}{2}$

....

(1)

(Total for Question 3 is 3 marks)

$\sqrt{xy^2}$ **ALGEBRA**

Revision Guide
Pages 9, 23

Hint

Multiply the numbers together and then multiply the letters.

Hint

Write t to the power 1 not 0.

LEARN IT!

When multiplying, add the powers.

$a^m \times a^n = a^{m+n}$

Hint

Add the terms in the **numerator** (the number above the the fraction line). Divide both the numerator and the **denominator** (the number beneath the fraction line) by 2 to simplify.

urn to page 147 for complete worked solutions to the questions on this page.

NUMBER

Revision Guide
Pages 4, 5, 61

Problem solved!

Plan your strategy:
- work out the total weight of 4 apples, 2 bananas and 3 peaches
- subtract this weight from the total weight
- divide the remaining weight by the weight of one orange.

LEARN IT!

$1 \text{kg} = 1000 \text{g}$

Watch out!

Read the question carefully and take care with all the calculations.

Hint

Work out the total weight of 15 tomatoes.

Watch out!

Use the same units when comparing the weights.

Hint

You must give a sensible realistic answer – think about the likely range in the weight of the tomatoes.

---

4 Ken buys some fruit.

He buys apples, bananas, peaches and oranges.
Ken buys

4 apples	weighing 125 g each
2 bananas	weighing 170 g each
3 peaches	weighing 135 g each

Each orange has a weight of 90 g.

The fruit has a total weight of 1.785 kg.

(a) Work out how many oranges Ken buys.

....
(3

Jane wants to buy 15 tomatoes.
She asks for 1 kg of tomatoes at a shop.
Jane assumes that each tomato has a weight of 75 g.

(b) (i) If Jane's assumption is correct, will she get 15 tomatoes?
You must show how you get your answer.

(2

(ii) If Jane's assumption is **not** correct, could she get 15 tomatoes?
Justify your answer.

....

....
(1

(Total for Question 4 is 6 marks

Turn to page 147 for complete worked solutions to the questions on this page.

60 students were asked how they get to school.

The table shows the results.

	Bus	Walk	Car	Bicycle
Number of students	15	27	12	6

(a) What fraction of the 60 students did **not** walk to school?

....
(2)

(b) Complete the pie chart for the information in the table.

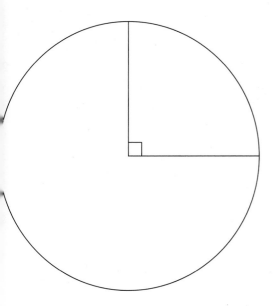

(4)

(Total for Question 5 is 6 marks)

urn to page 147 for complete worked solutions to the questions on this page.

RATIO AND PROPORTION

Revision Guide
Page 59

Hint

Add the values in the ratio to find the total number of parts.

Hint

The total number of parts is given by the denominator of the fraction.

Watch out!

Make sure you write your ratio in the order given in the question.

NUMBER

Revision Guide
Page 11

LEARN IT!

A **prime number** can be divided by only 1 and itself.

Watch out!

Make sure you answer the question with 'yes' or 'no' once you have shown your method.

---

6   Annie and Lily share some money in the ratio 4 : 3

(a) What fraction of the money does Lily get?

....

(1

Rosie and Dan share some sweets.

Dan gets $\frac{1}{4}$ of the sweets.

(b) Write down the ratio of the number of sweets Rosie gets to the number of sweets Dan gets.

....

(1

(Total for Question 6 is 2 marks

---

7   Steve says,

"There are more prime numbers between 20 and 30 than there are between 10 and 20"

Is Steve right?
You must show how you get your answer.

(Total for Question 7 is 2 marks

Turn to page 148 for complete worked solutions to the questions on this page

PROBABILITY AND STATISTICS

Chrissy drew this graph to show the percentage of buses that got to a bus stop on time for six months.

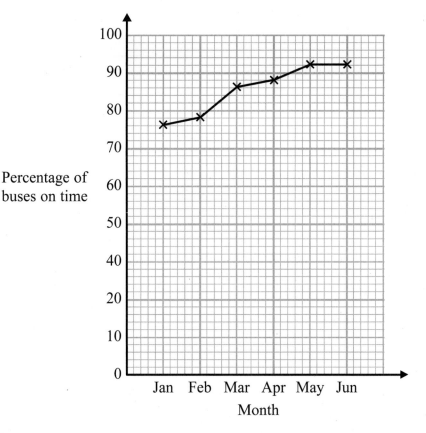

Percentage of buses on time

Month

Revision Guide Page 123

(a) Write down **one** thing that is wrong with the graph.

....

(1)

(b) Describe the trend in the percentage of buses that got to the bus stop on time.

....

(1)

(Total for Question 8 is 2 marks)

Hint

Look carefully at the axes.

Hint

Is the graph line going up, going down or neither?

LEARN IT!

Always look at the **overall pattern** of the graph to identify a **trend**.

GEOMETRY AND MEASURES

Revision Guide
Pages 98, 102

Hint

Measure the distance from Backley to Cremford using a ruler. Then multiply by 0.5.

LEARN IT!

The **scale** tells you which units to measure the distance in and what they represent.

Watch out!

In scale questions, do **not** round up or down unless the question asks you to.

Hint

Work out which bearing you need to find (**from** where **to** where?).

LEARN IT!

Always measure **bearings** clockwise from the north line. Bearings always have 3 digits.

Watch out!

Use a **protractor** and make sure the zero line is placed on the north line.

---

9 Here is a map of an island.

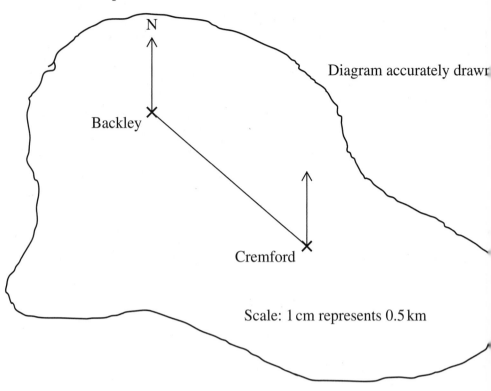

Diagram accurately drawn

Scale: 1 cm represents 0.5 km

A straight road joins the two villages, Backley and Cremford.

(a) Work out the real distance between the two villages.

.... km

(2

(b) Find the bearing of Cremford from Backley.

....

(1

(Total for Question 9 is 3 marks

Turn to page 148 for complete worked solutions to the questions on this page.

0 The diagram shows two shapes drawn on a centimetre grid.

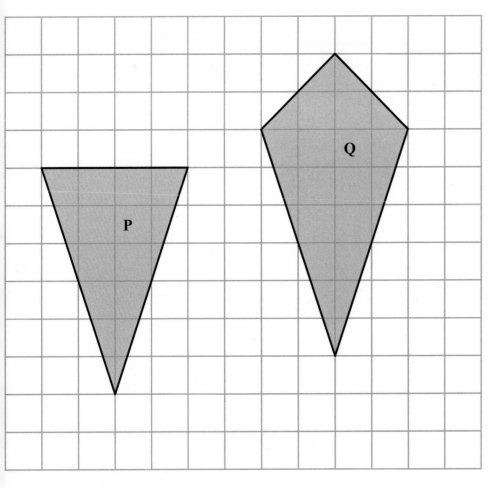

(a) Find the area of shape **P**.

....
(2)

(b) Write down the mathematical name of quadrilateral **Q**.

....
(1)

(Total for Question 10 is 3 marks)

urn to page 148 for complete worked solutions to the questions on this page.

GEOMETRY AND MEASURES

Revision Guide
Pages 72, 80

Hint

Write down the base and vertical height of the triangle.

LEARN IT!

Area of triangle
$= \dfrac{\text{base} \times \text{height}}{2}$

Watch out!

Use the formula to find the area. Don't count the squares in shape **P**.

LEARN IT!

You must learn the names of different 2D shapes.

NUMBER

 Revision Guide
Pages 4, 5, 59

Problem solved!

Plan your strategy:
- work out the income from the quiz and from membership fees
- write the three incomes as a ratio in the order stated in the question
- cancel, if possible, by dividing each part by a common factor
- continue to cancel until there are no more common factors.

LEARN IT!

A ratio is in its **simplest form** when it has been cancelled down completely and the parts do not share a common factor.

Watch out!

It is easy to make a mistake, so write down your working even if you are using a calculator. You might be awarded a mark for your working.

---

11 The table shows a cricket club's income in 2016 from a fete, a quiz and membership fees.

	Income	
Fete		£250
Quiz	Entry fees Refreshments	13 at £5 each £35
Membership fees		25 at £20 each

Express as a ratio

the income from the fete to the income from the quiz to the income from membership fees.

Give your ratio in its simplest form.

....

(Total for Question 11 is 3 marks)

Turn to page 149 for complete worked solutions to the questions on this page.

2 200 people live in a village.

23 people do **not** have a garden.
10 males do **not** have a garden.
95 people are male.

(a) Use this information to complete the frequency tree.

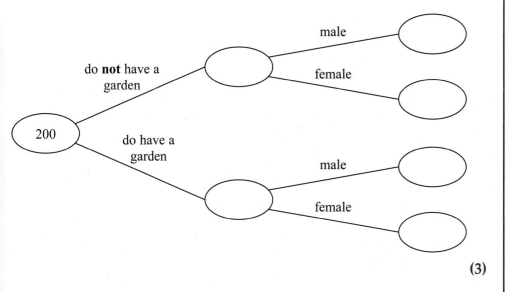

(3)

 PROBABILITY AND STATISTICS

Revision Guide
Pages 127, 130

Problem solved!

1. Write down the number of people who **do not** have a garden.

2. Use this to write down the number who **do** have a garden on the first branch.

3. Write down the number of **males** who **do not** have a garden.

4. Use this to work out the number of **females** who **do not** have a garden.

5. Use the **total** number of males to work out the number of **males**. who **have** a garden.

6. Use this to work out the number of **females** who **have** a garden.

One of the people who does **not** have a garden is chosen at random.

(b) Write down the probability that this person is female.

Hint

The person is chosen at random from those who do not have a garden, not from the total.

LEARN IT!

Probability =
number of successful outcomes
————————
total number of possible outcomes

....
(2)

(Total for Question 12 is 5 marks)

NUMBER

Revision Guide
Page 7

Hint

Work out the hourly rate for Ellie by multiplying the number of hats she makes per hour by the amount she is paid for each hat.

Hint

Work out Reaze's hourly rate by dividing the total paid by the number of hours worked.

LEARN IT!

£1 = 100p

13 Ellie makes hats.
She makes at least 17 hats per hour.
She is paid 46p for each hat she makes.

Reaze is a waiter.
He works 35 hours and is paid a total of £266

Show that Ellie's hourly rate of pay is more than Reaze's hourly rate of pay.

(Total for Question 13 is 3 marks

Turn to page 149 for complete worked solutions to the questions on this page.

a and b are odd numbers.

(a) Give an example to show that the value of $2(a + b)$ is a multiple of 4

(2)

(b) Show that, when a and b are both odd numbers, the value of $2(a + b)$ will always be a multiple of 4

(2)

(Total for Question 14 is 4 marks)

 ALGEBRA

Revision Guide
Page 52

Hint

Write down a and b as the sum of any two odd numbers of your choice.

LEARN IT!

The sum of any two odd numbers is always even.

Hint

Write down two odd numbers in terms of n.

LEARN IT!

You can write any odd number as $2n - 1$ or $2n + 1$.

Explore

Define a and b differently, for example let $a = 2n + 1$ and $b = 2n + 3$. Can you still show a proof?

NUMBER

Revision Guide
Pages 5, 6

Hint

Read the question carefully to extract information correctly.

Problem solved!

Plan your strategy.
Work out:
- the number of litres to completely fill the tank in November
- the capacity of the tank
- the number of litres used to completely fill the tank in February
- the new price of one litre of oil
- the cost of oil in February.

Watch out!

You must work in either pounds or pence.

---

15 Mr Page uses oil to heat his home.

At the beginning of November there were 1000 litres of oil in his oil tank.

Mr Page bought enough oil to fill the tank completely.
He paid 50p per litre for this oil.
He paid a total amount of £750

At the end of February Mr Page had 600 litres of oil in the tank.
He bought enough oil to fill the tank completely.
The cost of oil had increased by 4%.

Work out the total amount Mr Page paid for the oil he bought in February.

£ ....

(Total for Question 15 is 5 mark

Solve $5x - 6 = 3(x - 1)$

$x = $ ....

(Total for Question 16 is 3 marks)

Emily buys a pack of 12 bottles of water.
The pack costs £5.64

Emily sells all 12 bottles for 50p each.

Work out Emily's percentage profit.
Give your answer correct to 1 decimal place.

.... %

(Total for Question 17 is 3 marks)

√xy² **ALGEBRA**

Revision Guide
Page 31

Hint

Multiply out the brackets first.

Watch out!

Make sure you apply the same operations to both sides of the equation.

% **RATIO AND PROPORTION**

Revision Guide
Pages 57, 58

Hint

Work the cost of one bottle and then find the profit made.

LEARN IT!

Percentage profit =
$\dfrac{\text{profit}}{\text{original price}} \times 100$

Watch out!

Always use the original price in the formula for percentage profit.

rn to page 150 for complete worked solutions to the questions on this page.

GEOMETRY
AND MEASURES

Revision Guide
Page 103

Hint

Work out the circumference of the circle; then divide this by the number of points.

LEARN IT!

Circumference of a circle = πd or 2πr

Watch out!

Don't confuse the **circumference** of a circle (the distance around the outside) with the **area** of a circle (the space inside).

Hint

Think about how the mean distance is calculated. Has anything changed?

LEARN IT!

Mean distance between points =

total distance walked
total number of points

---

18 Hasmeet walks once round a circle with diameter 80 metres.

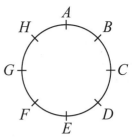

There are 8 points equally spaced on the circumference of the circle.

(a) Find the distance Hasmeet walks between one point and the next point.

....

(

Four of the points are moved, as shown in the diagram below.

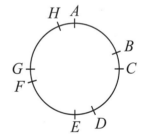

Hasmeet walks once round the circle again.

(b) Has the mean distance that Hasmeet walks between one point and the next point changed?
You must give a reason for your answer.

....

....

(

(Total for Question 18 is 3 mark

Turn to page 150 for complete worked solutions to the questions on this page

There are only blue cubes, yellow cubes and green cubes in a bag.

There are

       twice as many blue cubes as yellow cubes
and   four times as many green cubes as blue cubes.

Hannah takes at random a cube from the bag.

Work out the probability that Hannah takes a yellow cube.

PROBABILITY AND STATISTICS

Revision Guide
Pages 59, 127

Hint

You need to find the ratio of the three colours before you can find the probability of a yellow cube.

Problem solved!

Plan your strategy:
- write down a statement about blue and yellow cubes
- write down a statement about green and blue cubes
- use this to make a statement about green and yellow cubes
- combine the statements to form a ratio and use the ratio to find the total number of parts
- work out the probability of taking a yellow cube.

....

(Total for Question 19 is 3 marks)

rn to page 150 for complete worked solutions to the questions on this page.

GEOMETRY AND MEASURES

Revision Guide
Pages 86, 88

Hint

Use tracing paper to rotate shape T.

LEARN IT!

'About the origin' means rotate the shape around (0, 0).

Explore

Does it make any difference if the shape is rotated 180° anticlockwise or 180° clockwise?

Hint

Move shape A 1 unit to the left and 3 units downwards.

LEARN IT!

$\begin{pmatrix} x \\ y \end{pmatrix}$ means move x units in the positive x-direction (to the right) and y units in the positive y-direction (up).

$\begin{pmatrix} -x \\ -y \end{pmatrix}$ means move x units in the negative x-direction (to the left) and y units in the negative y-direction (down).

20

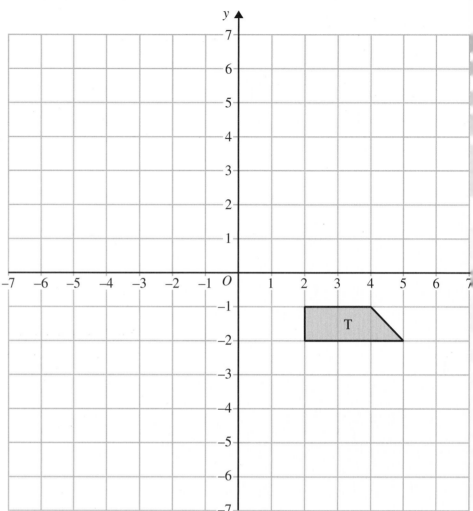

(a) Rotate trapezium **T** 180° about the origin.
    Label the new trapezium **A**.

(b) Translate trapezium **T** by the vector $\begin{pmatrix} -1 \\ -3 \end{pmatrix}$
    Label the new trapezium **B**.

(Total for Question 20 is 2 mark

Turn to page 151 for complete worked solutions to the questions on this page

$p^3 \times p^x = p^9$

(a) Find the value of x.

$x = \underline{\quad 6 \quad}$

(1)

$(7^2)^y = 7^{10}$

(b) Find the value of y.

$y = \underline{\quad 5 \quad}$

(1)

$100^a \times 1000^b$ can be written in the form 10^w

(c) Show that $w = 2a + 3b$

(2)

(Total for Question 21 is 4 marks)

rn to page 151 for complete worked solutions to the questions on this page.

√xy² ALGEBRA

Revision Guide
Page 24

LEARN IT!

$a^n \times a^m = a^{n+m}$

LEARN IT!

$(a^n)^m = a^{n \times m}$

Hint

Ignore the number 7s and concentrate on solving the y equation.

Hint

Rewrite each term as 10 to an equivalent power. Then use index rules.

**GEOMETRY
AND MEASURES**

Revision Guide
Pages 90, 92

Hint

Draw a vertical line
to split the trapezium
into a small and
large triangle, and a
rectangle.

Problem solved!

1. Use Pythagoras'
theorem to find the
length of the side of
the small triangle.

2. Use this value and
the length of the
rectangle to find the
length of the large
triangle.

3. Use trigonometry to
work out angle CDA.

LEARN IT!

Pythagoras' theorem
states:

$$a^2 + b^2 = c^2$$

LEARN IT!

Trigonometric ratios
are:

- $\sin x = \dfrac{opp}{hyp}$
- $\cos x = \dfrac{adj}{hyp}$
- $\tan x = \dfrac{opp}{adj}$

---

22 *ABCD* is a trapezium.

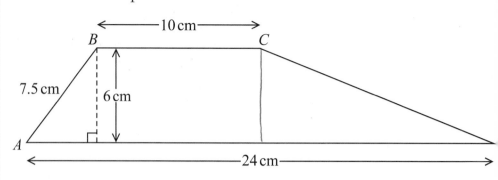

Work out the size of angle *CDA*.
Give your answer correct to 1 decimal place.

$7 \cdot 5^2 = 56 \cdot 25$

$6^2 = 36$

$56 \cdot 25 - 36 = 20 \cdot 25$

$\sqrt{20 \cdot 25} = 4 \cdot 5$

$24 - 4 \cdot 5 = 19 \cdot 5 - 10 = 9 \cdot 5$

....

(Total for Question 22 is 5 mark

Turn to page 151 for complete worked solutions to the questions on this page

3 Use your calculator to work out $\sqrt{\dfrac{\sin 25° + \sin 40°}{\cos 25° - \cos 40°}}$

(a) Write down all the figures on your calculator display.

....

(2)

(b) Write your answer to part (a) correct to 2 decimal places.

....

(1)

(Total for Question 23 is 3 marks)

NUMBER

Revision Guide
Pages 3, 16

Hint

You can enter this in one go into your calculator by using the fraction button ⬚, but remember to apply the correct priority (order) of operations.

Problem solved!

In part (b), when rounding to 2 decimal places look at the digit in the third decimal place:
• if it is 5 or more, add 1 to the second digit (round up)
• if is less than 5, do not change the second digit (round down).

Watch out!

Read the question carefully. You must round to the correct number of decimal places. Do not confuse rounding to **decimal places** with **significant figures**.

...urn to page 151 for complete worked solutions to the questions on this page.

$\sqrt{xy^2}$ **ALGEBRA**

 Revision Guide
Pages 8, 28, 46

LEARN IT!

Since both $a \times a = a^2$
and $-a \times -a = a^2$,
$\sqrt{a^2} = a$ and $-a$.
So $\sqrt{a^2} = \pm a$

Hint

Use the acronym **FOIL**
to multiply out the
terms. FOIL means:
- **F**irst terms
- **O**uter terms
- **I**nner terms
- **L**ast terms

Watch out!

$x \times x = x^2$

LEARN IT!

$(x + a)(x + b)$
$= x^2 + bx + ax + ab$

Hint

You need to find two
numbers that add up to
6 and multiply to give
9. Both of them must
be positive.

Hint

A quadratic expression
has two brackets, so
write your answer as
$(x + ...)(x + ...)$.

---

24 (a) Solve $2x^2 = 72$

....

(2

(b) Expand and simplify $(2x + 1)(3x - 2)$

....

(2

(c) Factorise $x^2 + 6x + 9$

....

(1

(Total for Question 24 is 5 marks

TOTAL FOR PAPER 2F IS 80 MARK

Turn to page 152 for complete worked solutions to the questions on this page

Paper 3F: Calculator
Time allowed: 1 hour 30 minutes

Write 3758 correct to the nearest 1000

....

(Total for Question 1 is 1 mark)

Simplify $y + 3y - 2y$

....

(Total for Question 2 is 1 mark)

NUMBER

Revision Guide
Page 3

Problem solved!

1. To round to the nearest thousand, look at the digit in the hundreds place.

2. If it is 5 or more, add 1 to the thousands digit (round up); if it is less than 5, do not change the thousands digit (round down).

3. Write zeros in the hundreds, tens and units places.

ALGEBRA

Revision Guide
Page 22

Hint

Simplify the expression fully and be careful with the minus sign.

NUMBER

Revision Guide
Page 11

Hint

Write down all the pairs of numbers that multiply to give 18.

LEARN IT!

The **factors** of a number are any whole numbers that divide into it exactly.

Watch out!

1 is a factor of every number.

Explore

Every number is a factor of itself.

3   Write down all the factors of 18

$$
\begin{array}{c}
1\ 8 \\
/\ \backslash \\
6\quad 3 \\
/\ \backslash \\
3\quad 2
\end{array}
$$

 6, 3, 2, 1, 18, 9

(Total for Question 3 is 2 marks)

Turn to page 153 for complete worked solutions to the questions on this page.

The table gives information about the prices of cinema tickets.

Cinema ticket	Price
adult ticket	£7.80
child ticket	£5.80
family ticket (for 4 people)	£24.30

Mr Edwards and his 3 children go to the cinema.

It is cheaper for Mr Edwards to buy 1 family ticket rather than 4 separate tickets.

(a) How much cheaper?

....
(3)

The film starts at 6.45 pm.
The film lasts 102 minutes.

(b) What time does the film finish?

....
(2)

(Total for Question 4 is 5 marks)

Problem solved!

Plan your strategy: work out the cost of the four tickets and then find the difference between the cost of the four tickets and the cost of the family ticket.

LEARN IT!

£1 = 100p

Watch out!

Read the question carefully – you must say how much **cheaper** the family ticket is. Use the correct units.

Hint

Break down the length of the film into hours and minutes. Then add on each step.

LEARN IT!

1 hour = 60 minutes

urn to page 153 for complete worked solutions to the questions on this page.

% RATIO AND PROPORTION

Revision Guide
Page 61

 LEARN IT!

1 litre = 1000 ml

Watch out!

The question states 'completely filled' so round down at the end.

PROBABILITY AND STATISTICS

Revision Guide
Page 116

Problem solved!

Plan your strategy:
- you know that 20 cycles were sold on Tuesday, Wednesday and Thursday
- use this to work out the number of cycles shown by one wheel
- work out how many wheels represent the cycles sold on Friday and on Saturday
- draw the number of wheels for each day
- complete the key.

Watch out!

Complete the key. A key to a pictogram must have a diagram.

---

5   Thais has a large bottle of shampoo.
    There are 2 litres of shampoo in the large bottle.

    Thais also has some empty small bottles.
    Each small bottle can be completely filled with 150 ml of shampoo.

    How many small bottles can be completely filled with shampoo from the large bottle?

    ....

    (Total for Question 5 is 3 marks)

6   The incomplete pictogram shows information about the number of cycles sold in a shop on Tuesday, on Wednesday and on Thursday.

		Key:
Tuesday	⊕	
Wednesday	⊕ ⊕ ◖	
Thursday	⊕ ◖	
Friday		
Saturday		

    A total of 20 cycles were sold on Tuesday, Wednesday and Thursday.

    8 cycles were sold on Friday.
    15 cycles were sold on Saturday.

    Use this information to complete the pictogram.

    (Total for Question 6 is 3 marks)

Turn to page 153 for complete worked solutions to the questions on this page.

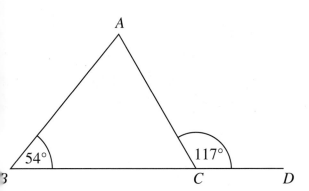

BCD is a straight line.
ABC is a triangle.

Show that triangle ABC is an isosceles triangle.
Give a reason for each stage of your working.

(Total for Question 7 is 4 marks)

GEOMETRY AND MEASURES

Revision Guide
Pages 73, 74

Hint

When you work out a missing angle, write it on the diagram.

LEARN IT!

You need to know the **properties of angles**:
- Angles on a straight line add up to 180°.
- Angles in a triangle add up to 180°.
- Base angles of an isosceles triangle are equal.

Watch out!

You must write down a reason when you have worked out the size of an angle.

Turn to page 154 for complete worked solutions to the questions on this page.

GEOMETRY AND MEASURES

Revision Guide
Pages 96, 98

Hint

You can use lengths that you are given to estimate other lengths. Use a ruler to measure the height of the tower in cm and the length of the bus in cm. Work out how many times the length of the bus goes into the height of the tower.

Watch out!

You need to show your working and explain what you are calculating at each stage.

8

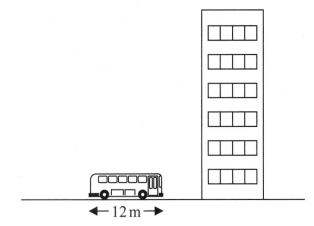

←— 12 m —→

The picture shows a bus next to a building.
The bus has a length of 12 m.

The bus and the building are drawn to the same scale.

Work out an estimate for the height, in metres, of the building.

....

(Total for Question 8 is 2 mark

Turn to page 154 for complete worked solutions to the questions on this page

Nidah writes down two different prime numbers.

She adds together her two numbers.
Her answer is a square number less than 30

Find two prime numbers that Nidah could have written down.

.... / ....

(Total for Question 9 is 2 marks)

Jim thinks of a number.

$\frac{2}{3}$ of Jim's number is 48

Work out $\frac{5}{6}$ of Jim's number.

....

(Total for Question 10 is 2 marks)

rn to page 154 for complete worked solutions to the questions on this page.

 NUMBER

 Revision Guide
Pages 8, 11

Hint

Start by writing a list a list of all the prime numbers less than 30 and all the square numbers less than 30.

LEARN IT!

A **prime number** has exactly two factors. It can be divided by only 1 and itself.

NUMBER

Revision Guide
Page 13

Hint

Jim's number must be greater than 48.

Hint

Use the fraction button on your calculator to work out $\frac{5}{6}$ of 72.

Watch out!

Read the question carefully and do one step at a time, showing your working clearly.

NUMBER

Revision Guide
Page 57

Hint

You can write 5% of 24 as $\frac{5}{100} \times 24$.

Problem solved!

Plan your strategy:
- work out the total cost of 11 driving lessons for offer 1
- for offer 2 work out 5% of £24
- subtract this value from the cost of the driving lesson
- multiply this value by the number of lessons
- compare your two totals and then answer the question.

Watch out!

Make sure you clearly state your final answer.

RATIO AND PROPORTION

Revision Guide
Pages 61, 67

Hint

Divide 3.60 by 2.5 to find the cost of 1kg of apples. Then find the cost of 3.5 kg of apples.

---

11 Jack's driving school has two offers.

Offer 1	**Offer 2**
First driving lesson free	All driving lessons
All other driving lessons normal price	5% off the normal price

The normal price of a driving lesson is £24

Douglas is going to have 12 driving lessons.

Which is the cheaper offer for 12 driving lessons, Offer 1 or Offer 2?
You must show how you get your answer.

(Total for Question 11 is 3 marks

---

12 2.5 kg of apples cost £3.60

Work out the cost of 3.5 kg of apples.

£ ....

(Total for Question 12 is 2 marks

Turn to page 154 for complete worked solutions to the questions on this page

(a) Complete the table of values for $y = \frac{1}{2}x - 1$

x	−2	−1	0	1	2	3
y	−2				0	

(2)

 ALGEBRA

Revision Guide
Page 38

Hint

To complete the table, substitute each value of x into the right-hand side of the equation and work out the corresponding y value.

LEARN IT!

You must know how to multiply positive and negative numbers:

$+ \times + = +$

$- \times - = +$

$+ \times - = -$

$- \times + = -$

(b) On the grid, draw the graph of $y = \frac{1}{2}x - 1$ for values of x from −2 to 3

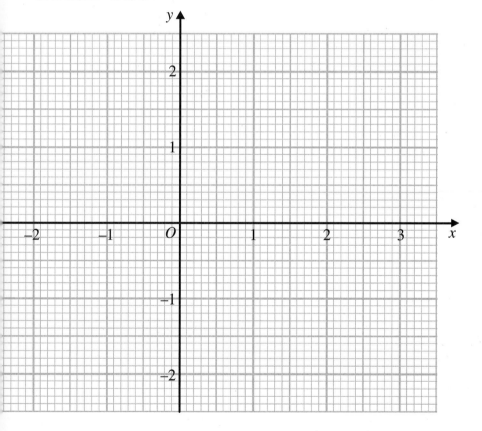

(2)

Watch out!

The graph should be a straight line. If any one of your points does not follow the pattern, check your working.

Hint

Read horizontally across from $y = 0.3$, then vertically down to the x-axis. The accuracy of your x-value will depend on the accuracy of your graph. Give your answer correct to one decimal place.

(c) Use your graph to find the value of x when $y = 0.3$

$x = $ ....

(1)

(Total for Question 13 is 5 marks)

rn to page 155 for complete worked solutions to the questions on this page.

GEOMETRY AND MEASURES

Revision Guide
Page 87

Hint

To describe this transformation fully, you need to write the name of the transformation and give the equation of the line.

LEARN IT!

There are four **types of transformation**: translation, reflection, rotation and enlargement.

RATIO AND PROPORTION

Revision Guide
Page 60

Problem solved!

1. Work out the cost of 1 m of cotton fabric.

2. Then work out the cost of the other lengths of cotton fabric.

3. You are given the ratio of 2 : 5 as the cost of cotton to the cost of silk, so multiply each length of cotton by $\frac{5}{2}$ to get the cost of each length of silk.

14

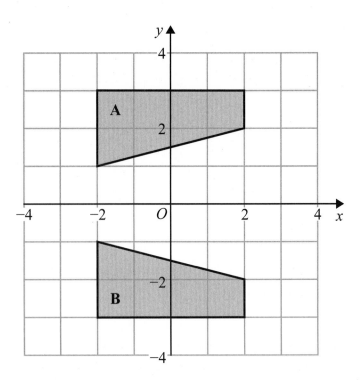

Describe fully the single transformation that maps shape **A** onto shape **B**.

....

(Total for Question 14 is 2 marks

15 The ratio of the cost of one metre of cotton fabric to the cost of one metre of silk fabric is 2 : 5

Complete the table of costs.

	2 m	6 m	8 m	9 m
cotton fabric	£6			
silk fabric				

(Total for Question 15 is 3 marks

Turn to page 155 for complete worked solutions to the questions on this page.

Chloe has a van.

She is going to use the van to deliver boxes.
Each box is a cuboid, 40 cm by 30 cm by 35 cm.

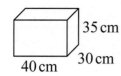

35 cm

30 cm

40 cm

The space for boxes in the van has

maximum length   2.4 m
maximum width   1.5 m
maximum height   1.4 m

The space for boxes is empty.
Chloe wants to put as many boxes as possible into the van.

She can put 3 boxes into the van in one minute.
Assume that the space for boxes is in the shape of a cuboid.

(a) Work out how many minutes it should take Chloe to
put as many boxes as possible into the van.

.... minutes
(4)

The space for boxes might **not** be in the shape of a cuboid.

(b) Explain how this could affect the time it would take
Chloe to put as many boxes as possible into the van.

....

....
(1)

(Total for Question 16 is 5 marks)

 GEOMETRY AND MEASURES

Revision Guide
Page 83

Hint

Use the same units in
all of your working.

LEARN IT!

1 m = 100 cm

Problem solved!

Plan your strategy:
• work out the exact
number of boxes that
fit along the length,
the width and the
height of the van
• find the total number
of boxes that will fit
by multiplying the
number of boxes
that fit along the
length, the width and
the height
• find the time taken by
dividing the number
of boxes by 3.

Hint

You must state 'more
time' or 'less time' with
a sensible reason.

rn to page 155 for complete worked solutions to the questions on this page.

 Revision Guide
Pages 22, 29

Hint

Factorise means to add in brackets. The first step of factorising is to identify a common factor and put it outside the bracket.

LEARN IT!

You must be able to recall and use correct mathematical language.

---

17 (a) Factorise $4m + 12$

$$4(m+3)$$

.....$4(m+3)$.....

expression	equation	formula	identity
inequality	term	factor	multiple

(b) Choose two words from the box above to make this statement correct.

$5y$ is a ...$term$... in the ...$expression$...

$3x + 5y$

(Total for Question 17 is 3 mark

---

116   Turn to page 155 for complete worked solutions to the questions on this page

8 Here is a sequence of patterns made with counters.

pattern number 1   pattern number 2   pattern number 3

(a) Find an expression, in terms of n, for the number of
    counters in pattern number n.

....
(2)

Bayo has 90 counters.

(b) Can Bayo make a pattern in this sequence using all 90
    of his counters?
    You must show how you get your answer.

(2)

(Total for Question 18 is 4 marks)

√xy² **ALGEBRA**

Revision Guide
Page 35

Hint

Work out the common
difference between
each term. Then
subtract the common
difference from the
first term to work out
the zero term.

LEARN IT!

nth term =

$\dfrac{\text{common}}{\text{difference}} \times n + \dfrac{\text{zero}}{\text{term}}$

Problem solved!

1. Make your nth term
equal to 90.

2. Solve the equation
for n.

3. If n is an **integer**
(whole number), then
Bayo can make a
pattern using all 90
counters; if n is not
an integer, then Bayo
cannot make a pattern
in this sequence using
all 90 counters.

urn to page 156 for complete worked solutions to the questions on this page.

PROBABILITY AND STATISTICS

Revision Guide
Pages 121, 122

Hint

Write down the cumulative frequency on the side of the table.

LEARN IT!

Median = $\left(\dfrac{n + 1}{2}\right)$th value for n data values in order.

Hint

To draw a frequency polygon you need to find the midpoint of each class interval. Then plot the midpoints and join the points using straight lines.

LEARN IT!

The **midpoint** of a class interval is the number halfway between the two given numbers in the class interval.

Watch out!

Don't join up the first point with the last point to make a polygon.

19 The table shows information about the heights of 80 children.

Height (h cm)	Frequency
$130 < h \leqslant 140$	4
$140 < h \leqslant 150$	11
$150 < h \leqslant 160$	24
$160 < h \leqslant 170$	22
$170 < h \leqslant 180$	19

(a) Find the class interval that contains the median.

....

(

(b) Draw a frequency polygon for the information in the table.

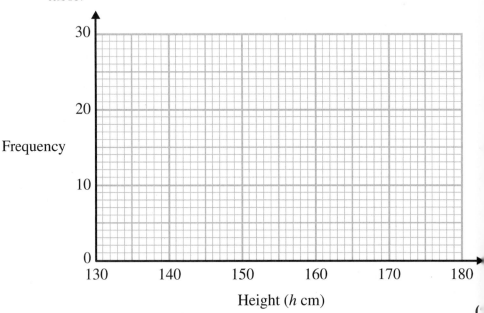

(

(Total for Question 19 is 3 mark

Turn to page 156 for complete worked solutions to the questions on this page

In London, 1 litre of petrol costs 108.9p
In New York, 1 US gallon of petrol costs $2.83

> 1 US gallon = 3.785 litres
> £1 = $1.46

In which city is petrol better value for money, London or New York?
You must show your working.

(Total for Question 20 is 3 marks)

A gold bar has a mass of 12.5 kg.

The density of gold is 19.3 g / cm³

Work out the volume of the gold bar.
Give your answer correct to 3 significant figures.

.... cm³

(Total for Question 21 is 3 marks)

rn to page 156 for complete worked solutions to the questions on this page.

% RATIO AND PROPORTION

Revision Guide Page 67

Hint

To compare values, you need to use consistent units – work in litres and dollars.

Problem solved!

Plan your strategy:
- work out the cost of 1 litre of petrol in dollars in London
- convert 1 gallon into litres
- work out the cost of 1 litre of petrol in dollars in New York
- compare the cost of 1 litre in each city
- write out your answer clearly.

GEOMETRY AND MEASURES

Revision Guide Page 65

Hint

Always write down the relevant formula. It can help to sketch a formula triangle.

LEARN IT!

1 kg = 1000 g

% RATIO AND PROPORTION

 Revision Guide
Page 60

LEARN IT!

$a:b$ and $b:c$ is the same as $a:b:c$.

Problem solved!

Plan your strategy:
- form a three-part ratio
- use your three-part ratio to work out the total number of parts
- work out the value of 1 part by dividing the quantity by the total number of parts
- multiply your answer by the number of parts representing red pens.

 NUMBER

Revision Guide
Page 16

Explore

When you multiply a number by its reciprocal the answer is 1.

Hint

If a number is rounded to 1 decimal place the error is ±0.05. To find the limits of the error interval, subtract 0.05 from the rounded number and add 0.05 to the rounded number.

---

22 There are only blue pens, green pens and red pens in a box.

The ratio of the number of blue pens to the number of green pens is 2 : 5
The ratio of the number of green pens to the number of red pens is 4 : 1

There are less than 100 pens in the box.

What is the greatest possible number of red pens in the box?

....

(Total for Question 22 is 3 marks

---

23 (a) Find the value of the reciprocal of 1.6
Give your answer as a decimal.

....

(

Jess rounds a number, x, to one decimal place.
The result is 9.8

(b) Write down the error interval for x.

....

(

(Total for Question 23 is 3 marks

Turn to page 156 for complete worked solutions to the questions on this page

Here is a rectangle.

The length of the rectangle is 7 cm longer than the width of the rectangle.

4 of these rectangles are used to make this 8-sided shape.

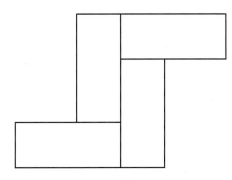

The perimeter of the 8-sided shape is 70 cm.

Work out the area of the 8-sided shape.

 $\sqrt{xy^2}$ **ALGEBRA**

Revision Guide
Pages 51, 79

Hint

You need to create an equation and solve it for x.

LEARN IT!

Area of rectangle
= length × width

Problem solved!

Plan your strategy:
• label the small rectangle in terms of x and use this to label the 8-sided shape
• find the perimeter of the shape in terms of x and make it equal to 70
• solve for x and use this to work out the width and length of the rectangle
• use the formula for the area of a rectangle.

Watch out!

You need to find the area of the 8-sided shape, not the single rectangle.

.... cm²

(Total for Question 24 is 5 marks)

NUMBER

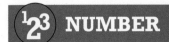

Revision Guide
Page 18

Hint

Use brackets and
the $\boxed{\times 10^x}$ button when
entering numbers in
standard form into
your calculator.

Watch out!

Write down your
calculation and count
decimal places carefully
when converting
between standard form
and ordinary numbers.

---

25 Work out $(13.8 \times 10^7) \times (5.4 \times 10^{-12})$
Give your answer as an ordinary number.

....

(Total for Question 25 is 2 marks

Turn to page 157 for complete worked solutions to the questions on this page

6 When a drawing pin is dropped it can land point down or point up.

Lucy, Mel and Tom each dropped the drawing pin a number of times.

The table shows the number of times the drawing pin landed point down and the number of times the drawing pin landed point up for each person.

	Lucy	Mel	Tom
point down	31	53	16
point up	14	27	9

Rachael is going to drop the drawing pin once.

(a) Whose results will give the best estimate for the probability that the drawing pin will land point up? Give a reason for your answer.

....

....

(1)

Stuart is going to drop the drawing pin twice.

(b) Use all the results in the table to work out an estimate for the probability that the drawing pin will land point up the first time and point down the second time.

....

(2)

(Total for Question 26 is 3 marks)

Turn to page 157 for complete worked solutions to the questions on this page.

$\sqrt{xy^2}$ **ALGEBRA**

Revision Guide
Page 49

Hint

It helps to number your equations to show what you are doing at different steps.

Problem solved!

Plan your strategy:
- choose a variable (x or y) to eliminate
- make the coefficient of your chosen variable the same in both equations; do this by multiplying through all the terms in one or both equations
- add or subtract to eliminate your chosen variable
- solve the resulting equation
- use the solution to work out the value of the other variable.

LEARN IT!

A **coefficient** is a number in front of x or y.

27 Solve the simultaneous equations

$$x + 3y = 12$$
$$5x - y = 4$$

$x = $ ....

$y = $ ....

(Total for Question 27 is 3 marks)

TOTAL FOR PAPER 3F IS 80 MARKS

Turn to page 157 for complete worked solutions to the questions on this page.

Paper 1F: Non-calculator
Time allowed: 1 hour 30 minutes

1 Work out the value of 2^4
$$2 \times 2 \times 2 \times 2 = 16$$

<u>   16   ✓   </u>

(Total for Question 1 is 1 mark)

2 Write 7.264 51 correct to 3 decimal places.
$$7.264\,\circled{5}1$$

<u>   7.265   ✓   </u>

(Total for Question 2 is 1 mark)

1

---

3 (a) Simplify $7 \times e \times f \times 8$
$$7 \times e \times f \times 8 = 7 \times 8 \times e \times f = 56ef$$

<u>   56ef   ✓   </u>
(1)

(b) Solve $\frac{x}{5} = 2\frac{1}{2}$

$$\frac{x}{5} = 2\frac{1}{2} = \frac{5}{2}$$
$$x = \frac{5}{2} \times 5 = \frac{25}{2} = 12.5$$

$x =$ <u>   12.5   ✓ </u>
(1)

(Total for Question 3 is 2 marks)

4 Write $\frac{4}{5}$ as a percentage.

$$\frac{4}{5} \times 100 = \frac{400}{5} = 80$$

<u>   80   ✓   </u>%

(Total for Question 4 is 1 mark)

2

---

5 Work out 60% of 70

$$60\% \text{ of } 70 = \frac{60}{100} \times 70 = 0.6 \times 70 \;✓$$
$$= 42$$

> Alternative acceptable answer:
> Find and use 10%:
> 10% = 7
> 60% = 7 × 6 = 42

<u>   42   ✓   </u>

(Total for Question 5 is 2 marks)

6 Sammy spins a fair 4-sided spinner.

(i) On the probability scale, mark with a cross (×) the probability that the spinner will land on **B**.

(1)

(ii) On the probability scale, mark with a cross (×) the probability that the spinner will land on **F**.

(1)

(Total for Question 6 is 2 marks)

3

---

7 Fahima buys

   2 packets of bread rolls costing £1.50 for each packet

   1 bottle of ketchup costing £1.60

   3 packets of sausages

Fahima pays with a £10 note.

She gets 30p change.

Fahima works out that one packet of sausages costs £2.30

Is Fahima right?

You must show how you get your answer.

$$2 \times 1.50 = 3.00$$
$$10.00 - (3.00 + 1.60 + 0.30) =$$
$$10.00 - 4.90 = 5.10 \;✓$$
$$5.10 \div 3 = 1.70 \;✓$$

Fahima is incorrect because one packet
of sausages costs £1.70 ✓

(Total for Question 7 is 3 marks)

8 (a) Work out $\frac{5}{8} \times \frac{3}{4}$

$$\frac{5}{8} \times \frac{3}{4} = \frac{5 \times 3}{8 \times 4} = \frac{15}{32}$$

<u> $\frac{15}{32}$ ✓ </u>
(1)

(b) Work out $\frac{2}{3} - \frac{1}{4}$

$$\frac{2}{3} = \frac{8}{12} \qquad\qquad \frac{1}{4} = \frac{3}{12}$$

$$\frac{8}{12} - \frac{3}{12} = \frac{8-3}{12} \;✓$$
$$= \frac{5}{12}$$

<u> $\frac{5}{12}$ ✓ </u>
(2)

(Total for Question 8 is 3 marks)

4

9 Sean works for a company.

His normal rate of pay is £12 per hour.

When Sean works more than 8 hours a day, he is paid overtime for each hour he works more than 8 hours.

Sean's rate of overtime pay per hour is $1\frac{1}{4}$ times his normal rate of pay per hour.

On Monday Sean worked for 10 hours.

Work out the total amount of money Sean earned on Monday.

$8 \times 12 = 96$ ✓

$10 - 8 = 2$ hours overtime

$1\frac{1}{4} = \frac{5}{4}$

$2 \times 12 \times \frac{5}{4} = \frac{120}{4} = 30$ ✓

Total $= 96 + 30$ ✓

$ = 126$

£ ......126...... ✓

(Total for Question 9 is 4 marks)

10 A farmer has 20 boxes of eggs.

There are 6 eggs in each box.

Write, as a ratio, the number of eggs in two boxes to the total number of eggs.

Give your answer in its simplest form.

Number of eggs in 2 boxes = 12

Total number of eggs = $6 \times 20 = 120$

2 boxes : total

$12 : 120$ ✓

$2 : 20$

$1 : 10$

......1 : 10...... ✓

(Total for Question 10 is 2 marks)

5

11 A sequence of patterns is made from circular tiles and square tiles ☐

Here are the first three patterns in the sequence.

pattern number 1   pattern number 2   pattern number 3

(a) How many square tiles are needed to make pattern number 6?

p1	p2	p3	p4	p5	p6	
1	4	9	16	25	36 ✓	......36...... ✓

(2)

(b) How many circular tiles are needed to make pattern number 20?

p1	p2	p3	...	p20
4	8	12 ✓		
1×4	2×4	3×4	...	$20 \times 4 = 80$

......80...... ✓

(2)

Derek says,

"When the pattern number is odd, an odd number of square tiles is needed to make the pattern."

(c) Is Derek right?

You must give reasons for your answer.

When pattern number n is odd, the number of square tiles will be odd because odd × odd = odd. Derek is right. ✓

Alternative acceptable answer:
- pattern number 1 has 1 square tile
- pattern number 3 has 9 square tiles
- pattern number 5 has 25 square tiles
- pattern number n has odd × odd = odd.

So Derek is right.

(2)

(Total for Question 11 is 6 marks)

6

12 There are only 7 blue pens, 4 green pens and 6 red pens in a box.

One pen is taken at random from the box.

Write down the probability that this pen is blue.

Number of blue pens = 7

Total number of pens = $7 + 4 + 6 = 17$ ✓

$P(\text{blue}) = \frac{7}{17}$

......$\frac{7}{17}$...... ✓

(Total for Question 12 is 2 marks)

13 The diagram shows a tree and a man.

The man is of average height.

The tree and the man are drawn to the same scale.

(a) Write down an estimate for the real height, in metres, of the man.

......1.7...... ✓ metres

(1)

Alternative acceptable answer:

A reasonable estimate is in the range 1.5–2 m.

(b) Find an estimate for the real height, in metres, of the tree.

Diagram: man measures approx. 1 cm and tree measures approx. 5 cm

So scale factor ≈ 5

Real height of tree = 5 × real height of man

$ = 5 \times 1.7$ ✓

$ = 8.5$

......8.5...... ✓ metres

(2)

Alternative acceptable answer:

Your answer will depend on your answer to part **(a)** and should be in the range 7.5–12 m.

(Total for Question 13 is 3 marks)

7

14 Year 9 students from Halle School were asked to choose one language to study.

The table shows information about their choices.

Language	Number of students		Angle
French	56	× 3	168
Spanish	40	× 3	120
German	24	× 3	72

(a) Draw an accurate pie chart to show this information.

Total number of students = $56 + 40 + 24 = 120$

1 student represents $360° \div 120 = 3°$

French: $56 \times 3° = 168°$

Spanish: $40 \times 3° = 120°$

German: $24 \times 3° = 72°$ ✓

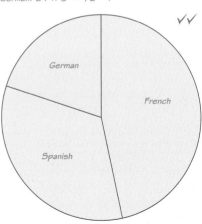

✓✓

Marking guidance:

1 mark for all three angles drawn ±2°.

1 mark for correct labels (languages).

(3)

8

126

Year 9 students from Lowry School were also asked to choose one language to study.

This accurate pie chart shows information about their choices.

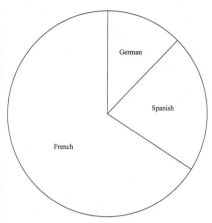

Shameena says,

"The pie chart shows that French was chosen by more Year 9 students at Lowry School than at Halle School."

(b) Is Shameena right?

You must explain your answer.

No, because information about the total number of students asked at Lowry is not provided. ✔

(1)

(Total for Question 14 is 4 marks)

9

---

15 Here are a triangle and a rectangle.

9 cm
8 cm
16 cm
width w

The area of the rectangle is 6 times the area of the triangle.

Work out the width of the rectangle.

area of triangle $= \frac{1}{2} \times 9 \times 8 = 36$ ✔

area of rectangle $= 16 \times w$

area of rectangle $= 6 \times$ area of triangle

$16 \times w = 6 \times 36$

$16 \times w = 216$ ✔

$w = \frac{216}{16}$ ✔

$= \frac{108}{8} = \frac{54}{4} = \frac{27}{2} = 13.5$

13.5 ✔ cm

(Total for Question 15 is 4 marks)

16 $v = u + at$

$u = 1 \quad a = -3 \quad t = \frac{1}{2}$

Work out the value of v.

$v = u + at$

$= 1 + (-3)\left(\frac{1}{2}\right)$

$= 1 - \frac{3}{2} = \frac{2}{2} - \frac{3}{2}$ ✔

$= -\frac{1}{2} = -0.5$

$v = $ $-\frac{1}{2}$ or -0.5 ✔

(Total for Question 16 is 2 marks)

10

---

17 5 tins of soup have a total weight of 1750 grams.

4 tins of soup and 3 packets of soup have a total weight of 1490 grams.

Work out the total weight of 3 tins of soup and 2 packets of soup.

Let t = weight of 1 tin of soup and p = weight of 1 packet of soup

$5t = 1750$

$t = \frac{1750}{5}$ ✔

$t = 350$

$4t + 3p = 1490$

$(4 \times 350) + 3p = 1490$

$1400 + 3p = 1490$

$3p = 1490 - 1400$ ✔

$3p = 90$

$p = \frac{90}{3}$

$p = 30$

Weight of 3 tins of soup and 2 packets of soup

$= 3t + 2p$

$= (3 \times 350) + (2 \times 30) = 1050 + 60$ ✔

$= 1110$

1110 ✔ grams

(Total for Question 17 is 4 marks)

11

---

18 Balena has a garden in the shape of a circle of radius 10 m.
He is going to cover the garden with grass seed to make a lawn.

10 m

Grass seed is sold in boxes.
Each box of grass seed will cover 46 m² of garden.

Balena wants to cover all the garden with grass seed.

(a) Work out an estimate for the number of boxes of grass seed Balena needs.

You must show your working.

Area of circle $= \pi r^2 = \pi \times r \times r$

$\approx 3 \times 10 \times 10$

$= 300$ ✔

Number of boxes $= 300 \div 46$ ✔

$\approx 300 \div 50$ ✔

$= 6$

6 ✔

(4)

(b) Is your estimate for part (a) an underestimate or an overestimate?

Give a reason for your answer.

It is an underestimate because the actual area is greater than the estimated area so more boxes would be needed. ✔

(1)

Alternative acceptable answer:

It is an underestimate because the actual area covered by one box has been rounded up, so more boxes would be needed.

(Total for Question 18 is 5 marks)

12

127

19 (a) Solve $4(x-5)=18$

$4(x-5)=18$

$4x-20=18$ ✓

$4x=18+20$

$4x=38$

$x=\dfrac{38}{4}=\dfrac{19}{2}=9.5$ $\qquad x=\underline{\quad 9.5 \quad}$ ✓

$\qquad\qquad\qquad\qquad\qquad\qquad\qquad$ **(2)**

$-3<t\leqslant 2$

t is an integer.

(b) Write down all the possible values of t.

~~−3~~ −2 −1 0 1 2 ✓

$\qquad\qquad\qquad\underline{-2 \; -1 \; 0 \; 1 \; 2}$ ✓

$\qquad\qquad\qquad\qquad\qquad\qquad$ **(2)**

(Total for Question 19 is 4 marks)

20 Azmol is paid £1500 per month.

He is going to get a 3% increase in the amount of money he is paid.

Work out how much money Azmol will be paid per month after the increase.

Increase $=$ 3% of $1500=\dfrac{3}{100}\times 1500=45$ ✓

New monthly pay $=1500+45=1545$

£$\underline{\quad 1545 \quad}$ ✓

(Total for Question 20 is 2 marks)

13   14

---

21 The scatter graph shows the maximum temperature and the number of hours of sunshine in fourteen British towns on one day.

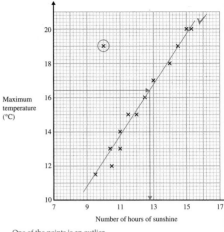

One of the points is an outlier.

(a) Write down the coordinates of this point.

($\underline{\quad 10 \quad}$ ✓ , $\underline{\quad 19 \quad}$ ✓)

$\qquad\qquad\qquad\qquad\qquad\qquad$ **(1)**

(b) For all the other points write down the type of correlation.

$\underline{\quad\text{positive} \quad}$ ✓

$\qquad\qquad\qquad\qquad\qquad\qquad$ **(1)**

On the same day, in another British town, the maximum temperature was 16.4°C.

(c) Estimate the number of hours of sunshine in this town on this day.

$\underline{\quad 12.8 \quad}$ ✓ .... hours

$\qquad\qquad\qquad\qquad\qquad\qquad$ **(2)**

> Marking guidance:
>
> 1 mark for a line of best fit
>
> 1 mark for answer in the range 12–13 hours, according to line of best fit. A **line of best fit** is a straight line as close to as many data points as possible.

A weatherman says,

   "Temperatures are higher on days when there is more sunshine."

(d) Does the scatter graph support what the weatherman says?

Give a reason for your answer.

Yes, because the temperature increases with

increasing hours of sunshine. ✓

$\qquad\qquad\qquad\qquad\qquad\qquad$ **(1)**

(Total for Question 21 is 5 marks)

22 Express 56 as the product of its prime factors.

$56=2\times 2\times 2\times 7$

✓

$\underline{\quad 2\times 2\times 2\times 7 \quad}$ ✓

(Total for Question 22 is 2 marks)

15   16

---

23 Work out $\quad 54.6\times 4.3$

```
    5 4 6
  ×   4 3
  1 6 3 8
2 1 8 4 0
─────────
2 3 4 7 8  ✓✓
```

$\underline{\quad 234.78 \quad}$ ✓

> Alternative acceptable answer:
>
> You could use the grid method:
>
> | × | 500 | 40 | 6 | Total |
> |---|---|---|---|---|
> | 40 | 20 000 | 1 600 | 240 | 21 840 |
> | 3 | 1 500 | 120 | 18 | 1 638 |
> | | | | | 23 478 |
>
> $546\times 43=23\,478$
>
> $54.6\times 4.3=234.78$

(Total for Question 23 is 3 marks)

24

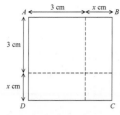

The area of square $ABCD$ is 10 cm².

Show that $x^2 + 6x = 1$

$AB = x + 3$

$AD = x + 3$

Area of $ABCD = (x + 3)(x + 3)$ ✓

$\qquad = x^2 + 3x + 3x + 9$

$\qquad = x^2 + 6x + 9$

$x^2 + 6x + 9 = 10$ ✓

$\qquad x^2 + 6x = 1$ ✓

(Total for Question 24 is 3 marks)

---

25 This rectangular frame is made from 5 straight pieces of metal.

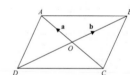

The weight of the metal is 1.5 kg per metre.

Work out the total weight of the metal in the frame.

Diagonal $= \sqrt{12^2 + 5^2}$ ✓

$\qquad = \sqrt{144 + 25} = \sqrt{169} = 13$ m ✓

Total length of frame $= 12 + 5 + 13 + 12 + 5$

$\qquad = 47$ m ✓

Weight of frame $= 47 \times 1.5$ ✓

$\qquad = (47 \times 1) + (47 \times 0.5)$

$\qquad = 47 + 23.5$

$\qquad = 70.5$

$\underline{\qquad 70.5 \qquad}$ ✓ kg

(Total for Question 25 is 5 marks)

---

26 The equation of the line L_1 is $y = 3x - 2$

The equation of the line L_2 is $3y - 9x + 5 = 0$

Show that these two lines are parallel.

Line L_1: gradient $= 3$ ✓

Line L_2:

$3y - 9x + 5 = 0$

$\qquad 3y = 9x - 5$

$\qquad y = \frac{9}{3}x - \frac{5}{3}$

$\qquad y = 3x - \frac{5}{3}$

Gradient of $L_2 = 3$ ✓

L_1 and L_2 are parallel because they have the same gradient.

(Total for Question 26 is 2 marks)

27

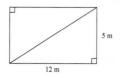

$ABCD$ is a parallelogram.

The diagonals of the parallelogram intersect at O.

$\overrightarrow{OA} = \mathbf{a}$ and $\overrightarrow{OB} = \mathbf{b}$

(a) Find, in terms of $\mathbf{b}$, the vector $\overrightarrow{DB}$.

$\overrightarrow{DB} = 2 \times \overrightarrow{OB} = 2 \times \underline{b}$

$\underline{\qquad 2\underline{b} \qquad}$ ✓

(1)

(b) Find, in terms of $\mathbf{a}$ and $\mathbf{b}$, the vector $\overrightarrow{AB}$.

$\overrightarrow{AB} = \overrightarrow{AO} + \overrightarrow{OB} = -\overrightarrow{OA} + \overrightarrow{OB}$

$\qquad = -\underline{a} + \underline{b} = \underline{b} - \underline{a}$

$\underline{\qquad \underline{b} - \underline{a} \qquad}$ ✓

(1)

(c) Find, in terms of $\mathbf{a}$ and $\mathbf{b}$, the vector $\overrightarrow{AD}$.

$\overrightarrow{AD} = \overrightarrow{AB} + \overrightarrow{BD} = \overrightarrow{AB} - \overrightarrow{DB}$

$\qquad = \underline{b} - \underline{a} - 2\underline{b} = -\underline{b} - \underline{a} = -\underline{a} - \underline{b}$

$\underline{\qquad -\underline{a} - \underline{b} \qquad}$ ✓

(1)

(Total for Question 27 is 3 marks)

TOTAL FOR PAPER 1F IS 80 MARKS

Paper 2F: Calculator
Time allowed: 1 hour 30 minutes

1 (a) Simplify $5p - 3p + p$

$5p - 3p + p = 2p + p = 3p$

$\underline{\qquad 3p \quad \checkmark}$
(1)

(b) Simplify $m^3 + m^3$

$m^3 + m^3 = 2m^3$

$\underline{\qquad 2m^3 \quad \checkmark}$
(1)

(c) Simplify $10 + 3c + 5d - 7c + d$

$10 + 3c + 5d - 7c + d = 10 + 3c - 7c + 5d + d$
$= 10 - 4c + 6d$

$\underline{\qquad 10 - 4c + 6d \quad \checkmark\checkmark}$
(2)

(Total for Question 1 is 4 marks)

2 Write 56.78 correct to one significant figure.

$5\underline{6}.78 \longrightarrow 60$

$\underline{\qquad 60 \quad \checkmark}$

(Total for Question 2 is 1 mark)

21

---

3 A teacher asks the students in Year 6 what type of transport they use to get to school.

The dual bar chart shows some of the results.

Key:
■ boys
▨ girls

(a) What is the most popular type of transport used by the boys?

$\underline{\qquad \text{walk} \quad \checkmark}$
(1)

7 girls walk to school.

(b) Show this information on the dual bar chart.
(1)

More of the students get to school by car than by bus.

(c) How many more?

Car: $9 + 5 = 14$

Bus: $6 + 4 = 10$

$14 - 10 = 4$

$\underline{\qquad 4 \quad \checkmark}$
(1)

The number of students in Year 5 is the same as the number of students in Year 6.

(d) What is the total number of students in Years 5 and 6?

Total in Year 6:

$5 + 9 + 6 + 4 + 9 + 7 + 4 + 1 + 2 + 1 = 48 \quad \checkmark$

$48 \times 2 = 96$

$\underline{\qquad 96 \quad \checkmark}$
(2)

(Total for Question 3 is 5 marks)

22

---

4 Here are four fractions.

$\dfrac{2}{5} \qquad \dfrac{11}{30} \qquad \dfrac{1}{2} \qquad \dfrac{7}{15}$

Write these fractions in order of size.
Start with the smallest fraction.

$\dfrac{2}{5} \qquad \dfrac{11}{30} \qquad \dfrac{1}{2} \qquad \dfrac{7}{15}$

$\dfrac{12}{30} \qquad \dfrac{11}{30} \qquad \dfrac{15}{30} \qquad \dfrac{14}{30} \quad \checkmark$

$2 \qquad 1 \qquad 4 \qquad 3$

$\underline{\dfrac{11}{30} \quad \dfrac{2}{5} \quad \dfrac{7}{15} \quad \dfrac{1}{2} \quad \checkmark}$

Alternative acceptable answer:

Convert the fractions either to decimals or to percentages and then put them in order.

$\dfrac{2}{5} = 0.4 = 40\%$

$\dfrac{11}{30} = 0.367 = 36.7\%$

$\dfrac{1}{2} = 0.5 = 50\%$

$\dfrac{7}{15} = 0.467 = 46.7\%$

(Total for Question 4 is 2 marks)

23

---

5 David sells CDs in a shop.

The tally chart shows information about the number of CDs David sold on Monday, on Tuesday and on Wednesday.

	Tally	Frequency
Monday	ЖЖ ЖЖ |||	12
Tuesday	ЖЖ ЖЖ ЖЖ |||	18
Wednesday	ЖЖ |||	8

(a) Write down **one** thing that is wrong with the tally chart.

The frequency and tally for Monday should be the same; the tally has 13 but the frequency has 12. $\checkmark$
(1)

David drew this pictogram to show the information for Tuesday and Wednesday.

Tuesday	◐◐◐◐◐
Wednesday	◐◐◐

Key: ◐ represents 3 CDs

(b) Write down **one** thing that is wrong with this pictogram.

The key has ◐ = 3 CDs which means ◖ = $1\frac{1}{2}$ CDs but you can't have $\frac{1}{2}$ a CD. $\checkmark$
(1)

Alternative acceptable answer:

The pictogram for Tuesday should show 18 CDs but it only shows 15

The pictogram for Wednesday should show 8 CDs but it only shows 7.5

(Total for Question 5 is 2 marks)

24

6 There are 495 coins in a bottle.

$\frac{1}{3}$ of the coins are £1 coins.

124 of the coins are 50p coins.

The rest of the coins are 20p coins.

Work out the total value of the 495 coins.

£1 coins	50p coins	20p coins
$\frac{1}{3}$ of 495	50p = £0.50	20p = £0.20
= 495 ÷ 3		
= 165 ✓	124 × £0.50	495 − 165 − 124
	= £62	= 206 ✓
165 × £1		
= £165		206 × £0.20
		= £41.20

Total value = £165 + £62 + £41.20 ✓
            = £268.20

£ 268.20 ✓

(Total for Question 6 is 4 marks)

25

7 The probability that a new fridge has a fault is 0.015.

What is the probability that a new fridge does **not** have a fault?

1 − 0.015 = 0.985

0.985 ✓

(Total for Question 7 is 1 mark)

8 Here is a list of numbers.

21 22 23 24 25 26 27 28 29

(a) From the numbers in the list, write down a square number.

5 × 5 = 25

25 ✓

(1)

(b) From the numbers in the list, write down a number that is a multiple of **both** 4 and 6.

multiples of 4: 4, 8, 12, 16, 20, (24), 28

multiples of 6: 6, 12, 18, (24)

24 ✓

(1)

(c) Write down all the prime numbers in the list.

23, 29 ✓

(1)

(Total for Question 8 is 3 marks)

26

9

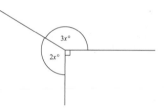

Find the value of x.

3x + 2x + 90 = 360 ✓

5x + 90 = 360

5x = 360 − 90

5x = 270

$x = \frac{270}{5}$ ✓

= 54

54 ✓

(Total for Question 9 is 3 marks)

27

10 Suha is going to buy 150 envelopes.

Here is some information about the cost of envelopes in two shops.

Letters2send	**Stationery World**
Pack of 25 envelopes for £3.49	Pack of 10 envelopes for £2.10 Buy 2 packs get 1 pack free

Suha wants to buy the envelopes as cheaply as possible.

Which shop should Suha buy the 150 envelopes from? You must show how you get your answer.

Letters2send

Number of packs:
150 ÷ 25 = 6 ✓

Cost = 6 × £3.49
     = £20.94 ✓

Stationery World

Number of packs needed:
150 ÷ 10 = 15

2 (+ 1) + 2 (+ 1) + 2 (+ 1) + 2 (+ 1) + 2 (+ 1) = 15

Buy 10 packs and get 5 free

Cost = 10 × £2.10
     = £21 ✓

£20.94 < £21

Suha should buy from Letters2send because £20.94 is less than £21 ✓

Alternative acceptable answer:

You could find the cost of 1 envelope first:

Letters2send

- cost of 1 envelope = 3.49 ÷ 25 = 0.1396
- cost of 150 envelopes = 0.1396 × 150
                        = 20.94

Stationery World

- buy 10 envelopes and receive 5 free
- cost of 1 envelope = 2.10 ÷ 15 = 0.14
- cost of 150 envelopes = 0.14 × 150 = 21

£20.94 < £21

Suha should buy from Letters2send because £20.94 is less than £21.

(Total for Question 10 is 4 marks)

28

131

11 You can use this graph to change between inches and centimetres.

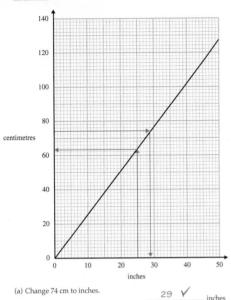

(a) Change 74 cm to inches.

29 ✓ inches
(1)

Marking guidance:

1 mark for answers in the range 29–30.

Daniel's height is 6 feet 3 inches.

1 foot = 12 inches

(b) What is Daniel's height in centimetres?

6 feet = 6 × 12 = 72 inches

72 inches + 3 inches = 75 inches ✓

75 = 25 × 3

25 inches = 63 cm

75 inches = (25 × 3) inches

= (63 × 3) cm ✓

= 189

Marking guidance:

Final mark for answers in the range 186–195

189 ✓ centimetres
(3)

(Total for Question 11 is 4 marks)

12 Find the value of $\dfrac{\sqrt{13.4 - 1.5}}{(6.8 + 0.06)^2}$

Write down all the figures on your calculator display.

$\dfrac{\sqrt{13.4 - 1.5}}{(6.8 + 0.06)^2} = \dfrac{\sqrt{11.9}}{6.86^2} = \dfrac{3.449637662}{47.0596}$ ✓

$= 0.07330359081$

0.07330359081 ✓

(Total for Question 12 is 2 marks)

13

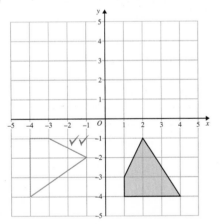

(a) Rotate shape **A** 90° clockwise about centre *O*.
(2)

Marking guidance:

1 mark for the quadrilateral in correct orientation (the right way up) and size.

1 mark for correct rotation clockwise about origin.

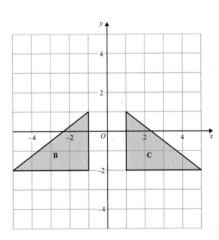

(b) Describe fully the single transformation that maps triangle **B** onto triangle **C**.

Reflection ✓

in the *y*-axis ✓
(2)

Alternative acceptable answer:

Reflection in the line *x* = 0

(Total for Question 13 is 4 marks)

14 (a) Factorise $5 - 10m$

$5 - 10m = 5(1 - 2m)$

$5(1 - 2m)$ ✓
(1)

(b) Factorise fully $2a^2b + 6ab^2$

$2a^2b + 6ab^2 = 2ab(a + 3b)$ ✓

$2ab(a + 3b)$ ✓
(2)

(Total for Question 14 is 3 marks)

15 (a) Write 4.7×10^{-1} as an ordinary number.

$4.7 \times 10^{-1} = 0.47$

0.47 ✓
(1)

(b) Work out the value of $(2.4 \times 10^3) \times (9.5 \times 10^5)$

Give your answer in standard form.

$(2.4 \times 10^3) \times (9.5 \times 10^5)$

$= 2.2\,8\,0\,0\,0\,0\,0\,0\,0$ ✓

$= 2.28 \times 10^9$

2.28×10^9 ✓
(2)

(Total for Question 15 is 3 marks)

16 A, B and C are three points on a map.

Marking guidance:

1 mark for perpendicular bisector.

i mark for circle centre A radius 2.5 cm.

1 mark for correct position of T.

1 cm represents 100 metres.

Point T is 250 metres from point A.
Point T is equidistant from point B and point C.

On the map, show one of the possible positions for point T.

(Total for Question 16 is 3 marks)

17 The table shows the probabilities that a biased dice will land on 2, on 3, on 4, on 5 and on 6.

Number on dice	1	2	3	4	5	6
Probability		0.17	0.18	0.09	0.15	0.1

Neymar rolls the biased dice 200 times.

Work out an estimate for the total number of times the dice will land on 1 or on 3.

$P(1) = 1 - (0.17 + 0.18 + 0.09 + 0.15 + 0.1)$ ✓

$= 1 - 0.69 = 0.31$

Number of 1s: $0.31 \times 200 = 62$ ✓

Number of 3s: $0.18 \times 200 = 36$

Number of 1s or 3s $= 62 + 36 = 98$

98 ✓

Alternative acceptable answer:

Using

(P event happens) = 1 − P(event does not happen):

$P(1 \text{ or } 3) = 1 - (0.17 + 0.09 + 0.15 + 0.1)$

$= 1 - 0.51 = 0.49$

Number of 1s or 3s: $0.49 \times 200 = 98$

(Total for Question 17 is 3 marks)

18 On Saturday, some adults and some children were in a theatre.
The ratio of the number of adults to the number of children was $5:2$

Each person had a seat in the Circle or had a seat in the Stalls.

$\frac{3}{4}$ of the children had seats in the Stalls.

117 children had seats in the Circle.

There are exactly 2600 seats in the theatre.

On this Saturday, were there people on more than 60% of the seats?
You must show how you get your answer.

$\frac{1}{4}$ represents 117 children

Number of children $= 4 \times 117 = 468$ ✓

2 parts $= 468$

1 part $= 468 \div 2 = 234$

5 parts $= 5 \times 234 = 1170$ ✓

Number of children and adults $= 1170 + 468$

$= 1638$ ✓

Percentage of seats occupied $= \frac{1638}{2600} \times 100$ ✓

$= 63\%$

$63\% > 60\%$

Yes, because 63% is greater than 60%. ✓

Alternative acceptable answer:

60% of $2600 = \frac{60}{100} \times 2600 = 1560$

Total number of children $= 1560 \times \frac{2}{7} = 445.714...$

Number of children in circle $= 445.714 \div 4$

$= 111.42... = 111$

Yes, because 111 is less than 117

(Total for Question 18 is 5 marks)

19 The diagram shows a prism with a cross section in the shape of a trapezium.

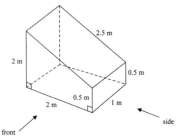

On the centimetre grid below, draw the front elevation and the side elevation of the prism.
Use a scale of 2 cm to 1 m.

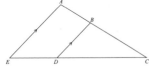

Marking guidance:	Marking guidance:
1 mark for trapezium with two right angles	1 mark for rectangle
1 mark for correct orientation/size	1 mark for correct orientation/size with solid line

(Total for Question 19 is 4 marks)

37

20 Olly drove 56 km from Liverpool to Manchester.

He then drove 61 km from Manchester to Sheffield.

Olly's average speed from Liverpool to Manchester was 70 km/h.

Olly took 75 minutes to drive from Manchester to Sheffield.

(a) Work out Olly's average speed for his total drive from Liverpool to Sheffield.

$$\text{speed} = \frac{\text{distance}}{\text{time}}$$

Liverpool to Manchester to Sheffield

56 km 61 km

70 km/h 75 minutes

Liverpool to Manchester: time $= \frac{56}{70}$ ✓

$= 0.8$ hours

Manchester to Sheffield:

75 minutes $= (75 \div 60)$ hours $= 1.25$ hours

Total distance $= 56 + 61 = 117$ km ✓

Total time $= 1.25$ hours $+ 0.8$ hours $= 2.05$ hours

$$\text{average speed} = \frac{\text{distance}}{\text{time}} = \frac{117}{2.05} ✓$$

$= 57.0731...$

≈ 57.1

57.1 ✓ km/h

(4)

Janie drove from Barnsley to York.

Janie's average speed from Barnsley to Leeds was 80 km/h.
Her average speed from Leeds to York was 60 km/h.

Janie says that the average speed from Barnsley to York can be found by working out the mean of 80 km/h and 60 km/h.

(b) If Janie is correct, what does this tell you about the two parts of Janie's journey?

The time taken for the two parts of the journey must be the same. ✓

(1)

(Total for Question 20 is 5 marks)

38

21

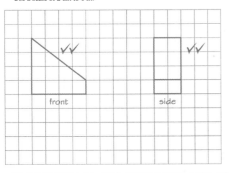

ABC and EDC are straight lines.

EA is parallel to DB.

EC = 8.1 cm.
DC = 5.4 cm.
DB = 2.6 cm.

(a) Work out the length of AE.

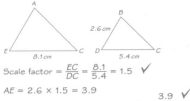

Scale factor $= \frac{EC}{DC} = \frac{8.1}{5.4} = 1.5$ ✓

$AE = 2.6 \times 1.5 = 3.9$

3.9 ✓ cm

(2)

AC = 6.15 cm.

(b) Work out the length of AB.

Scale factor $= 1.5$

$BC = 6.15 \div 1.5 = 4.1$ ✓

$AB = 6.15 - 4.1 = 2.05$

2.05 ✓ cm

(2)

(Total for Question 21 is 4 marks)

39

22 Anil wants to invest £25 000 for 3 years in a bank.

Personal Bank	**Secure Bank**
Compound Interest	Compound Interest
2% for each year	4.3% for the first year
	0.9% for each extra year

Which bank will give Anil the most interest at the end of 3 years?
You must show all your working.

Personal Bank

$25\,000 \times 1.02 \times 1.02 \times 1.02$ ✓

$= 25\,000 \times 1.02^3$

$= 26\,530.20$

£26 530.20 < £26 546.46

Secure Bank

$25\,000 \times 1.043 \times 1.009 \times 1.009$ ✓

$= 25\,000 \times 1.043 \times 1.009^2$

$= 26\,546.46$

Anil should invest in the Secure Bank because £26 546.46 is greater than £26 530.20. ✓

Alternative acceptable answer:

You could calculate only the interest.

- Personal Bank: interest after 3 years
  $= 500 + 510 + 520.20 = £1530.20$

- Secure Bank: interest after 3 years
  $= 1075 + 234.68 + 236.79 = £1546.47$

£1530.20 < £1546.47

so Anil should invest in the Secure Bank

(Total for Question 22 is 3 marks)

23 A number, n, is rounded to 2 decimal places.
The result is 4.76.

Using inequalities, write down the error interval for n.

$0.01 \div 2 = 0.005$ 4.76 ± 0.005

$4.76 - 0.005 = 4.755$

and $4.76 + 0.005 = 4.765$ ✓

$4.755 \leq n < 4.765$ ✓

(Total for Question 23 is 2 marks)

40

134

24 Solve $x^2 + 5x - 24 = 0$

$8 \times (-3) = -24$

$8 + (-3) = 5$

$(x + 8)(x - 3) = 0$ ✓✓

either:

$x + 8 = 0$ or $x - 3 = 0$

      $x = -8$ or $x = 3$

$$x = -8, \quad x = 3 \quad ✓$$

(Total for Question 24 is 3 marks)

41

---

25 Here are the first six terms of an arithmetic sequence.

$$3 \quad 8 \quad 13 \quad 18 \quad 23 \quad 28$$

(a) Find an expression, in terms of n, for the nth term of this sequence.

$$-2 \quad 3 \quad 8 \quad 13 \quad 18 \quad 23 \quad 28$$
$$-5 \quad +5 \quad +5 \quad +5 \quad +5 \quad +5$$

common difference is 5 so $5n$ ✓

zero term $= 3 - 5 = -2$

nth term is $5n - 2$

$$5n - 2 \quad ✓$$
           (2)

The nth term of a different sequence is $3n^2$
Nathan says that the 4th term of this sequence is 144.

(b) Is Nathan right?
Show how you get your answer.

when $n = 4$: $3n^2 = 3 \times n \times n = 3 \times 4 \times 4 = 48$

$48 \neq 144$

No he is not right. ✓

           (1)

Alternative acceptable answer:

If Nathan is right, then $n = 4$ when 4th term is 144:

$144 \div 3 = 48$

$\sqrt{48} = 6.9...$ which means $n \neq 4$

So he is not right.

(Total for Question 25 is 3 marks)

TOTAL FOR PAPER 2F IS 80 MARKS

42

Paper 3F: Calculator
Time allowed: 1 hour 30 minutes

1 The table shows the lengths of five rivers.

River	Length (km)
Trent	297
Don	112
Severn	354
Thames	346
Mersey	113

(a) Write down the rivers in order of length.

Start with the shortest river.

Don   Mersey   Trent
Thames   Severn ✓

(1)

Ami says,

"The River Thames is more than three times as long as the River Don."

(b) Show that Ami is correct.

River Don is 112 km and River Thames is 346 km

$3 \times 112 = 336$ $346 > 336$ Ami is correct ✓

(1)

(Total for Question 1 is 2 marks)

43

2 Cups are sold in packs and in boxes.

There are 12 cups in each pack.
There are 18 cups in each box.

Alison buys p packs of cups and b boxes of cups.

Write down an expression, in terms of p and b, for the total number of cups Alison buys.

Number of cups in p packs $= 12 \times p = 12p$ ✓
Number of cups in b boxes $= 18 \times b = 18b$
Total number of cups $= 12p + 18b$

$12p + 18b$ ✓

(Total for Question 2 is 2 marks)

3 Here are four digits.

5   6   1   9

(i) Write down the smallest possible two digit number that can be made with two of the digits.

The smallest digits are 1 and 5

15 ✓

(1)

(ii) Write down the three digit number closest to 200 that can be made with three of the digits.

169, ⓪196

196 ✓

(1)

(Total for Question 3 is 2 marks)

44

4 $\frac{4}{5}$ of a number is 32

Find the number.

$32 \div 4 = 8$ ✓
$8 \times 5 = 40$

40 ✓

(Total for Question 4 is 2 marks)

5 A path is made of white tiles and grey tiles.

$\frac{1}{4}$ of the tiles are white.

(a) Write down the ratio of white tiles to grey tiles.

$\frac{1}{4}$ of the tiles are white so $\frac{3}{4}$ of the tiles are grey

white tiles : grey tiles

1 : 3

1 : 3 ✓

(1)

There is a total of 56 tiles.

(b) Work out the number of grey tiles.

$\frac{3}{4}$ of the tiles are grey

Number of grey tiles $= \frac{3}{4} \times 56$ ✓
$= 42$

42 ✓

(2)

(Total for Question 5 is 3 marks)

45

6 Here is a list of numbers.

12   15   14   17   22   19   13

Bridgit says,

"To work out the median you find the middle number, so the median of these numbers is 17"

Bridgit's answer is **not** correct.

(a) What is wrong with Bridgit's method?

Bridgit needs to put the numbers in
numerical order first. ✓

(1)

(b) Work out the range of the numbers in the list.

Range = highest number – lowest number
$= 22 – 12$ ✓
$= 10$

10 ✓

(2)

(c) Work out the mean of the numbers in the list.

Sum of all values
$= 12 + 15 + 14 + 17 + 22 + 19 + 13$
$= 112$

7 values in total

Mean $= \frac{112}{7}$ ✓
$= 16$

16 ✓

(2)

(Total for Question 6 is 5 marks)

46

7 Priti is going to have a meal.

She can choose one starter and one main course from the menu.

Menu	
Starter	**Main Course**
Salad	Pasta
Fish	Rice
Melon	Burger

Write down all the possible combinations Priti can choose.

SP, SR, SB

FP, FR, FB

MP, MR, MB ✓✓

(Total for Question 7 is 2 marks)

8 Joanne wants to buy a dishwasher.

The dishwasher costs £372

Joanne will pay a deposit of £36
She will then pay the rest of the cost in 4 equal monthly payments.

How much is each monthly payment?

372 – 36 = 336

Monthly payment = 336 ÷ 4 ✓

= 84

£ _____84_____ ✓

(Total for Question 8 is 2 marks)

9 Davos is a cleaner.

The table shows information about the time it will take him to clean each of four rooms in a house.

Room	Time
Kitchen	2 hours
Sitting room	1 hour 40 minutes
Bedroom	$1\frac{1}{2}$ hours
Bathroom	45 minutes

Davos wants to clean all four rooms in one day.

He will have breaks for a total time of 75 minutes.

Davos is going to start cleaning at 9 am.

Will he finish cleaning by 4 pm?

You must show all your working.

Kitchen: 2 hours = 120 minutes ✓

Sitting room: 1h 40 min = 100 minutes

Bedroom: $1\frac{1}{2}$ = 90 minutes

Bathroom: 45 minutes

Total working time: 120 + 100 + 90 + 45
= 355 minutes

Time at house = working time + break time
= 355 + 75 = 430 minutes ✓

430 minutes = 420 minutes + 10 minutes
= 7 hours 10 minutes

9 am + 7 hours 10 minutes = 4:10 pm

No, Davos will not be finished by 4 pm ✓

> Alternative acceptable answer:
>
> 9 am → 4 pm = 7 hours
>
> 7 × 60 = 420 minutes
>
> Total working time
>
> = 120 + 100 + 90 + 45 = 355 minutes
>
> 355 + 75 = 430 minutes, so, no, he will not

(Total for Question 9 is 3 marks)

10 ABC is a straight line.

The length AB is five times the length BC.
$AC = 90$ cm.

Work out the length AB.

AB : BC

5 : 1 ✓

Total number of parts = 5 + 1 = 6

6 parts = 90

1 part = 90 ÷ 6

1 part = 15

AB = 5 × 15 = 75 ✓

_____75_____ ✓ cm

(Total for Question 10 is 3 marks)

11 $T = 4v + 3$

(a) Work out the value of T when $v = 2$

$T = 4v + 3$

$= 4 × 2 + 3$ ✓

$= 8 + 3 = 11$

$T = $ _____11_____ ✓

(2)

(b) Make v the subject of the formula $T = 4v + 3$

$T = 4v + 3$

$4v + 3 = T$ ✓

$4v = T - 3$

$v = \dfrac{T - 3}{4}$

$v = \dfrac{T - 3}{4}$ ✓

(2)

(Total for Question 11 is 4 marks)

12 The diagram shows a cube of side length 2 cm.

2 cm, 2 cm, 2 cm

Vera says,

"The volume of any solid made with 6 of these cubes is 48 cm³"

(a) Is Vera correct?
You must show your working.

Volume of cube = 2 × 2 × 2 = 8 cm³ ✓

Volume of 6 cubes = 8 × 6 = 48 cm³

Yes, Vera is correct. ✓

(2)

(b) (i) Draw a cuboid that can be made with 6 of these cubes.
Write the dimensions of the cuboid on your diagram.

2 cm, 4 cm, 6 cm

(1)

> Alternative acceptable answer:
>
> A cuboid with edges labelled 2 cm, 12 cm and 2 cm

(ii) Work out the surface area of your cuboid.

Surface area = (6 × 4) + (6 × 4) + (2 × 4)
+ (2 × 4) + (6 × 2) + (6 × 2) ✓

= 24 + 24 + 8 + 8 + 12 + 12

= 88

_____88_____ cm²

(2)

> Alternative acceptable answer:
>
> A 12 × 2 × 2 cuboid has surface area
>
> = 24 + 24 + 4 + 4 + 24 + 24 = 104 cm²

(Total for Question 12 is 5 marks)

13 The size of the largest angle in a triangle is 4 times the size of the smallest angle.
The other angle is 27° less than the largest angle.

Work out, in degrees, the size of each angle in the triangle.
You must show your working.

Let smallest angle = $x°$

largest angle = $4 \times x° = 4x°$

third angle = $4x° - 27°$ ✓

$x + 4x + 4x - 27 = 180$ ✓

$9x - 27 = 180$ ✓

$9x = 180 + 27$

$9x = 207$

$x = \dfrac{207}{9}$ ✓

$x = 23$

Smallest angle = $x° = 23°$

Largest angle = $4 \times x° = 4 \times 23° = 92°$

Third angle = $4x° - 27° = 92° - 27° = 65°$

.....23..... ° , ...92..... ° , ...65..... ✓ °

(Total for Question 13 is 5 marks)

51

14 Andy went on holiday to Canada.
His flights cost a total of £1500

Andy stayed for 14 nights.
His hotel room cost £196 per night.

Andy used wifi for 12 days.
Wifi cost $5 per day.

The exchange rate was $1.90 to £1

(a) Work out the total cost of the flights, the hotel room and wifi.
Give your answer in pounds.

Cost of flights = £1500

Cost of hotel = $14 \times \$196 = \$2744$ ✓

Cost of wifi = $12 \times \$5 = \$60$ ✓

Cost of hotel + wifi = $\$2744 + \$60 = \$2804$

$\$2804 \div 1.90 = £1475.79$ ✓

Total cost = £1500 + £1475.79 ✓

= £2975.79

£.....2975.79..... ✓

(5)

> Alternative acceptable answer:
>
> You could convert the cost of the hotel and the cost of the wifi into pounds separately.
>
> Cost of hotel = $14 \times \$196 = \$2744$
>
> $\$2744 \div 1.90 = £1444.21$
>
> Cost of wifi = $12 \times \$5 = \$60$
>
> $\$60 \div 1.90 = £31.58$
>
> Total cost in pounds
> = £1500 + £1444.21 + £31.58 = £2975.79

(b) If there were fewer dollars to £1, what effect would this have on the total cost, in pounds, of Andy's holiday?

The total cost will increase. ✓

(1)

> Alternative acceptable answer:
>
> Flight prices remain the same but the other prices will increase so the total cost will increase.

(Total for Question 14 is 6 marks)

52

15 $\mathscr{E} = \{$odd numbers less than 30$\}$

$A = \{3, 9, 15, 21, 27\}$

$B = \{5, 15, 25\}$

(a) Complete the Venn diagram to represent this information.

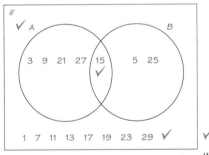

(4)

$\mathscr{E} = 1, 3, 5, 7, 9, 11, 13, 15, 17, 19, 21, 23,$
$25, 27, 29$

A number is chosen at random from the universal set, $\mathscr{E}$.

(b) What is the probability that the number is in the set $A \cup B$?

Number of elements in sets A and B = $4 + 1 + 2$

= 7

Total number of elements in universal set = 15

$P(A \cup B) = \dfrac{7}{15}$

$\dfrac{7}{15}$ ✓✓

(2)

(Total for Question 15 is 6 marks)

53

16 Solve the simultaneous equations

$$3x + y = -4$$
$$3x - 4y = 6$$

$3x + y = -4$ ①

$3x - 4y = 6$ ②

① − ② $y - (-4y) = -4 - 6$ ✓

$5y = -10$

$y = \dfrac{10}{5} = -2$

Substitute $y = -2$ into $3x + y = -4$ ✓.

$3x - 2 = -4$

$3x = -4 + 2$

$3x = -2$

$x = -\dfrac{2}{3}$

$x = $ .....$-\dfrac{2}{3}$..... ✓

$y = $ .....-2..... ✓

(Total for Question 16 is 3 marks)

54

138

17 The table shows some information about the dress sizes of 25 women.

Dress size	Number of women	
8	2	2
10	9	11
12	8	19
14	6	25
	25	

(a) Find the median dress size.

Median $= \frac{1}{2}(n+1)$th value $= \frac{1}{2}(25+1)$th value

$\qquad\qquad\qquad = 13$th value

$2 + 9 = 11$ values are in dress sizes 8 and 10

so the 13th value is in dress size 12

$\underline{\qquad 12 \qquad}$ ✓

(1)

3 of the 25 women have a shoe size of 7

Zoe says that if you choose at random one of the 25 women, the probability that she has either a shoe size of 7 or a dress size of 14 is $\frac{9}{25}$ because

$$\frac{3}{25} + \frac{6}{25} = \frac{9}{25}$$

(b) Is Zoe correct?

You must give a reason for your answer.

No, because the events are not mutually exclusive – a woman could be size 14 and take size 7 shoes. ✓

(1)

(Total for Question 17 is 2 marks)

---

18 Daniel bakes 420 cakes.

He bakes only vanilla cakes, banana cakes, lemon cakes and chocolate cakes.

$\frac{2}{7}$ of the cakes are vanilla cakes.

35% of the cakes are banana cakes.

The ratio of the number of lemon cakes to the number of chocolate cakes is $4:5$

Work out the number of lemon cakes Daniel bakes.

Number of vanilla cakes $= \frac{2}{7} \times 420 = 120$ ✓

Number of banana cakes $= 35\%$ of 420

$= \frac{35}{100} \times 420 = 147$ ✓

Total number of lemon cakes and chocolate cakes

$= 420 - 120 - 147 = 153$ ✓

lemon : chocolate
$\quad 4 : 5$

Total number of parts $= 4 + 5 = 9$

9 parts $= 153$

1 part $= \frac{153}{9} = 17$

Lemon cakes make up 4 parts of ratio:

$4 \times 17 = 68$
✓

$\underline{\qquad 68 \qquad}$ ✓

(Total for Question 18 is 5 marks)

---

19 In the diagram, *AB*, *BC* and *CD* are three sides of a regular polygon **P**.

Show that polygon **P** is a hexagon.
You must show your working.

Exterior angle of regular 12-sided polygon

$= 360° \div 12 = 30°$ ✓

Interior angle $= 180° - 30° = 150°$

Angle DCB $= 360° - 90° - 150° = 120°$ ✓

So interior angle of P $= 120°$

For a regular hexagon, exterior angle $= 360° \div 6$

$\qquad\qquad\qquad\qquad\qquad = 60°$ ✓

Interior angle $= 180° - 60° = 120°$

Therefore P must be hexagon ✓

(Total for Question 19 is 4 marks)

---

20 The density of apple juice is 1.05 grams per cm³.

The density of fruit syrup is 1.4 grams per cm³.

The density of carbonated water is 0.99 grams per cm³.

25 cm³ of apple juice are mixed with 15 cm³ of fruit syrup and 280 cm³ of carbonated water to make a drink with a volume of 320 cm³.

Work out the density of the drink.
Give your answer correct to 2 decimal places.

$\text{density} = \frac{\text{mass}}{\text{volume}}$

$\text{mass} = \text{density} \times \text{volume}$

Mass of apple juice $= 1.05 \times 25 = 26.25$ g ✓

Mass of fruit syrup $= 1.4 \times 15 = 21$ g

Mass of carbonated water $= 0.99 \times 280 = 277.2$ g

Total mass $= 26.25 + 21 + 277.2 = 324.45$ g ✓

Total volume $= 320$ cm³

$\text{density} = \frac{\text{mass}}{\text{volume}} = \frac{324.45}{320}$ ✓

$\qquad\qquad = 1.013\ 906\ 25$

$\qquad\qquad = 1.01$ (2 d.p.)

$\underline{\qquad 1.01 \qquad}$ ✓ g/cm³

(Total for Question 20 is 4 marks)

21

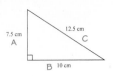

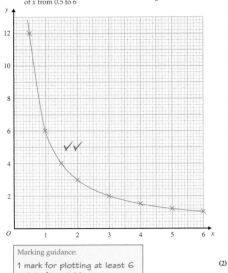

Show that these two triangles are mathematically similar.

A and a: 7.5 ÷ 3 = 2.5 ✓

B and b: 10 ÷ 4 = 2.5

C and c: 12.5 ÷ 5 = 2.5

All pairs of corresponding sides are enlarged
by the same scale factor. ✓

Alternative acceptable answer:

You could use trigonometry to show that the
angles in both triangles are equal (90°, 36.9° and
53.1°), and so the triangles are mathematically
similar.

(Total for Question 21 is 2 marks)

22 (a) Complete the table of values for $y = \dfrac{6}{x}$

$y = \dfrac{6}{0.5} = 12 \quad \dfrac{6}{1.5} = 4 \quad \dfrac{6}{3} = 2 \quad \dfrac{6}{5} = 1.2 \quad \dfrac{6}{6} = 1$

x	0.5	1	1.5	2	3	4	5	6
y	12	6	4	3	2	1.5	1.2	1

Marking guidance:

1 mark for 3 or 4 correct.
1 mark for all correct.

✓✓

(2)

(b) On the grid below, draw the graph of $y = \dfrac{6}{x}$ for values
of x from 0.5 to 6

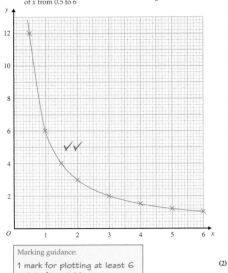

Marking guidance:

1 mark for plotting at least 6
points from table.
1 mark for fully correct curve.

(2)

(Total for Question 22 is 4 marks)

23 Harley's house has a value of £160 000 correct to 2
significant figures.

(a) (i) Write down the least possible value of the house.

10 000 ÷ 2 = 5000

160 000 – 5000 = 155 000

£ 155 000 ✓

(1)

(ii) Write down the greatest possible value of the house.

160 000 + 5000 = 165 000

£ 165 000 ✓

(1)

Alternative acceptable answer:

160 000 + 4999 = 164 999 or
160 000 + 4999.99 = 164 999.99

The value of Rita's house increased by 5%.
Her house then had a value of £210 000

(b) Work out the value of Rita's house before the increase.

100% + 5% = 105%

105% = 210 000 ✓

$1\% = \dfrac{210\,000}{105}$

$100\% = \dfrac{210\,000}{105} \times 100$

= 200 000

£ 200 000 ✓

(2)

Alternative acceptable answer:

You could use a multiplier.

Multiplier = (100% + 5%) ÷ 100 = 1.05

$100\% = \dfrac{210\,000}{1.05} = £200\,000$

(Total for Question 23 is 4 marks)

A total mark of 158 for
papers 1F, 2F and 3F
would have given you a
grade 5 in June 2017.

TOTAL FOR PAPER 3F IS 80 MARKS

Paper 1: Non-calculator
Time allowed: 1 hour 30 minutes

1 (a) Change 365 cm into metres.

$365 \div 100 = 3.65$

3.65 ✓ m
(1)

(b) Change 2.7 kg into grams.

$2.7 \times 1000 = 2700$

2700 ✓ g
(1)

(Total for Question 1 is 2 marks)

2 Work out $2 + 7 \times 10$

$2 + 70 = 72$

72 ✓

(Total for Question 2 is 1 mark)

3 Solve $\frac{y}{4} = 10.5$

$\frac{y}{4} = 10.5$

$y = 4 \times 10.5 = 42$

$y = $ 42 ✓

(Total for Question 3 is 1 mark)

4 Here are four numbers.
  −9 −2 2 9

Write one of these numbers in each box to make a correct calculation.

$\boxed{-9} + \boxed{2} = -7$ ✓

(Total for Question 4 is 1 mark)

5 Here are the first four terms of a number sequence.

   2   5   11   23

The rule to continue this sequence is

   multiply the previous term by 2 and then add 1

Work out the 5th term of this sequence.

$23 \times 2 = 46$
$46 + 1 = 47$

47 ✓

(Total for Question 5 is 1 mark)

6 Here are five straight rods.

←a−1→ ←a→ ←a→ ←a→ ←a + 4→

All measurements are in centimetres.

The total length of the five rods is L cm.

Find a formula for L in terms of a.
Write your formula as simply as possible.

$a - 1 + a + a + a + a + 4$ ✓

$L = a - 1 + a + a + a + a + 4$ ✓
$= 5a + 3$

$L = 5a + 3$ ✓

(Total for Question 6 is 3 marks)

7

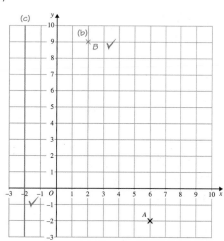

(a) Write down the coordinates of the point A.

(6 , −2 ✓)
(1)

141

(b) (i) Plot the point with coordinates (2, 9).
Label this point *B*.

(1)

(ii) Does point *B* lie on the straight line with equation
$y = 4x + 1$?
You must show how you get your answer.

$y = 4x + 1$ If $x = 2$

$$y = 4 \times 2 + 1$$
$$y = 8 + 1$$
$$y = 9$$

Yes, *B* lies on the line with equation $y = 4x + 1$ ✓

(1)

> Alternative acceptable answer:
>
> Draw the straight line $y = 4x + 1$ on the grid to show that the line goes through point *B* (2, 9).

(c) On the grid, draw the line with equation $x = -2$

(1)

(Total for Question 7 is 4 marks)

8   The length of a rectangle is twice as long as the width of the rectangle.
The area of the rectangle is 32 cm².

Draw the rectangle on the centimetre grid.

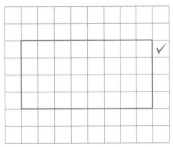

1 × 32
2 × 16
4 × 8 ✓

(Total for Question 8 is 2 marks)

66

9   Jacqui wants to work out $3480 \div 5$

She knows that $3480 \div 10 = 348$

Jacqui writes $3480 \div 5 = 174$

because $10 \div 5 = 2$

and $348 \div 2 = 174$

What mistake did Jacqui make in her method?

Jacqui should have multiplied 348 by 2
not divided by 2. ✓

(Total for Question 9 is 1 mark)

10   Jake and Sarah each played a computer game six times.

Their scores for each game are shown below.

| **Jake** | 10 | 9 | 8 | 11 | 12 | 8 |
| **Sarah** | 2 | 10 | 7 | 14 | 4 | 10 |

(a) Who had the most consistent scores, Jake or Sarah?
You must give a reason for your answer.

Jake, as his scores are closer together. ✓

(1)

Jake played a different game 20 times.

The stem and leaf diagram shows information about his scores.

0	9
1	2 3 3 4 5
2	5 6 6 6 6 7
3	1 3 4 6 8
4	0 2 9

Key
1 | 2 represents 12 points

Jake said his modal score was 6 points because 6 occurs most often in the diagram.

(b) Is Jake correct?
You must explain your answer.

Jake is not correct because he has not
considered the stem. ✓

(1)

> Alternative acceptable answer:
>
> Jake is not correct because the modal score is 26.

(Total for Question 10 is 2 marks)

68

11   There are 30 children in a nursery school.
At least 1 adult is needed for every 8 children in the nursery.

(a) Work out the least number of adults needed in the nursery.

8
$8 + 8 = 16$
$8 + 8 + 8 = 24$
$8 + 8 + 8 + 8 = 32$ ✓   4 ✓

(2)

> Alternative acceptable answer:
>
> You could do $30 \div 8 = 3.75$ and round up.

2 more children join the nursery.

(b) Does this mean that more adults are needed in the nursery?
You must give a reason for your answer.

$30 + 2 = 32$

$32 \div 8 = 4$ so no more adults are needed ✓

(1)

(Total for Question 11 is 3 marks)

12   Emma has 45 rabbits.

30 of the rabbits are male.
8 of the female rabbits have short hair.
12 of the rabbits with long hair are male.

(a) Use the information to complete the two-way table.

	Male	Female	Total
Long hair	12	7	19
Short hair	18	8	26
Total	30	15	45

$30 - 12 = 18$ ✓✓✓ **(3)**
$45 - 30 = 15$
$15 - 8 = 7$
$12 + 7 = 19$
$18 + 8 = 26$

> **Marking guidance:**
> 1 mark for a correct row or column.
> 1 mark for 5–8 correct figures in table.
> 1 mark for fully correct table.

One of Emma's rabbits is chosen at random.

(b) Write down the probability that this rabbit is a female with short hair.

Number of females with short hair = 8

Total number of rabbits = 45

Probability = $\frac{8}{45}$

$\frac{8}{45}$ ✓

(1)

(Total for Question 12 is 4 marks)

---

13 The total surface area of a cube is 294 cm².

Work out the volume of the cube.

Area of one face = 294 ÷ 6 = 49 ✓

Length of one side = $\sqrt{49}$ = 7 ✓

Volume of cube = length × width × height

$= 7 \times 7 \times 7$ ✓

$= 343$

343 ✓ cm³

(Total for Question 13 is 4 marks)

70

---

14 Here are two fractions.

$$\frac{7}{5} \qquad \frac{5}{7}$$

Work out which of the fractions is closer to 1
You must show all your working.

$\frac{5}{7} = \frac{25}{35}$ ✓ $\qquad 1 = \frac{35}{35} \qquad \frac{7}{5} = \frac{49}{35}$ ✓

$35 - 25 = 10$ and $49 - 35 = 14$

$10 < 14$

$\frac{5}{7}$ is closer to 1 ✓

(Total for Question 14 is 3 marks)

---

15 There are only red buttons, yellow buttons and orange buttons in a jar.
The number of red buttons, the number of yellow buttons and the number of orange buttons are in the ratio 7 : 4 : 9

Work out what percentage of the buttons in the jar are orange.

$7 + 4 + 9 = 20$

Orange buttons = $\frac{9}{20} \times 100$ ✓

45 ✓ %

(Total for Question 15 is 2 marks)

71

---

16 Berenika wants to buy 35 T-shirts.

Each T-shirt costs £5.80
Berenika does the calculation $40 \times 6 = 240$ to estimate the cost of 35 T-shirts.

(a) Explain how Berenika's calculation shows the actual cost will be less than £240

Berenika overestimates both the number of T-shirts
and the cost of each T-shirt so the actual cost
will be less than her estimate. ✓

(1)

There is a special offer.

T-shirts £5.80 each.

Buy 30 or more T-shirts.
Get 10% off the total cost.

(b) Work out the actual cost of buying 35 T-shirts using the special offer.

10 T-shirts = 5.80 × 10 = 58

5 T-shirts = 58 ÷ 2 = 29

35 T-shirts = 58 + 58 + 58 + 29 = 203 ✓

10% of 203 = 20.30 ✓

Cost of 35 T-shirts = 203 − 20.30 ✓

£ 182.70 ✓

(4)

Alternative acceptable answer:

10% of 5.80 = 0.58

Cost of 1 T-shirt after reduction:
1 T-shirt = 5.80 − 0.58 = 5.22

Cost of 10 T-shirts = 10 × 5.22 = 52.20

Cost of 5 T-shirts = 26.10

Cost of 35 T-shirts

= 52.20 + 52.20 + 52.20 + 26.10

= £182.70

(Total for Question 16 is 5 marks)

72

---

17 There are 3 cards in Box **A** and 3 cards in Box **B**.
There is a number on each card.

Box **A**   Box **B**

Ryan takes at random a card from Box **A** and a card from Box **B**.

He adds together the numbers on the two cards to get a total score.

Work out the probability that the total score is an odd number.

$3 + 9 = 12 \qquad 3 + 2 = 5 \qquad 3 + 3 = 6$

$4 + 9 = 13 \qquad 4 + 2 = 6 \qquad 4 + 3 = 7$

$5 + 9 = 14 \qquad 5 + 2 = 7 \qquad 5 + 3 = 8$ ✓

Number of odd scores = 4

Total number of scores = 9

Probability(odd score) = $\frac{4}{9}$

$\frac{4}{9}$ ✓

(Total for Question 17 is 2 marks)

73

143

18 Harry, Regan and Kelan share £450 in the ratio 2 : 5 : 3

How much money does Kelan get?

Total parts = 2 + 5 + 3 = 10

10 parts = 450

1 part = 450 ÷ 10 = 45 ✓

Kelan's share = 3 × 45 = 135

£ ....135.... ✓

Alternative acceptable answer:

Total parts = 2 + 5 + 3 = 10

Kelan's share = $\frac{3}{10}$ × 450 = 3 × 45 = 135

(Total for Question 18 is 2 marks)

19 Here is a list of ingredients for making 16 flapjacks.

Ingredients for 16 flapjacks

120 g butter
140 g brown sugar
250 g oats
2 tablespoons syrup

Jenny wants to make 24 flapjacks.

Work out how much of each of the ingredients she needs.

Alternative acceptable answer:

You could also work out the scale factor.

Scale factor for 24 flapjacks

= $\frac{24}{16}$ = 1.5

Ingredient	8 flapjacks	16 flapjacks	24 flapjacks
butter	120 ÷ 2 = 60	120	180 g
brown sugar	140 ÷ 2 = 70	140	210 g
oats	250 ÷ 2 = 125	250	375 g
syrup	2 ÷ 2 = 1	2	3 tablespoons

✓ ✓

butter ....180.... g
brown sugar ....210.... g
oats ....375.... g
syrup ....3.... ✓ tablespoons

Marking guidance:

1 mark for finding any correct amount for 8 flapjacks

1 mark for any correct amount for 24 flapjacks

1 mark for all answers correct

(Total for Question 19 is 3 marks)

20 Ami and Josh use a calculator to work out $\frac{595}{4.08^2 + 5.3}$

Ami's answer is 27.1115
Josh's answer is 271.115

One of these answers is correct.

Use approximations to find out which answer is correct.

$\frac{595}{4.08^2 + 5.3} \approx \frac{600}{4^2 + 5} = \frac{600}{21}$ ✓

$= \frac{600}{20} = 30$ ✓

Ami is correct because her answer is closer to 30 than Josh's answer is. ✓

(Total for Question 20 is 3 marks)

21 Work out $\frac{0.06 \times 0.0003}{0.01}$

Give your answer in standard form.

$\frac{0.06 \times 0.0003}{0.01} = \frac{6 \times 10^{-2} \times 3 \times 10^{-4}}{1 \times 10^{-2}}$ ✓

$= \frac{18 \times 10^{-6}}{1 \times 10^{-2}}$

$= 18 \times 10^{-4}$ ✓

$= 1.8 \times 10^{-3}$

1.8×10^{-3} ✓

(Total for Question 21 is 3 marks)

22 (a) Work out $\frac{2}{5} + \frac{1}{4}$

$\frac{2}{5} = \frac{8}{20}$ and $\frac{1}{4} = \frac{5}{20}$

$\frac{8}{20} + \frac{5}{20} = \frac{8 + 5}{20}$ ✓

$\frac{13}{20}$ ✓

(2)

(b) Write down the value of 2^{-3}

$2^{-3} = \frac{1}{2^3} = \frac{1}{8}$

$\frac{1}{8}$ ✓

(1)

(Total for Question 22 is 3 marks)

23 Write 36 as a product of its prime factors.

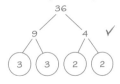

$2 \times 2 \times 3 \times 3$ ✓

(Total for Question 23 is 2 marks)

24 Kiaria is 7 years older than Jay.
Martha is twice as old as Kiaria.
The sum of their three ages is 77

Find the ratio of Jay's age to Kiaria's age to Martha's age.

Let Jay = x

Kiaria = $x + 7$

Martha = $2(x + 7)$ ✓

$x + x + 7 + 2(x + 7) = 77$ ✓

$x + x + 7 + 2x + 14 = 77$

$4x + 21 = 77$

$4x = 77 - 21$

$4x = 56$

$x = \frac{56}{4}$

$x = 14$ ✓

Jay = 14, Kiaria = 14 + 7 = 21,
Martha = 2 × 21 = 42

$14 : 21 : 42$ ✓

(Total for Question 24 is 4 marks)

25

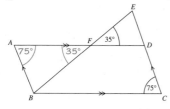

ABCD is a parallelogram.
EDC is a straight line.
F is the point on *AD* so that *BFE* is a straight line.

Angle *EFD* = 35°
Angle *DCB* = 75°

Show that angle *ABF* = 70°
Give a reason for each stage of your working.

Angle *AFB* = 35° because vertically opposite angles are equal. ✓

Angle *BAF* = 75° because opposite angles in a parallelogram are equal. ✓

Angle *ABF* = 180° − 35° − 75° because angles in a triangle sum to 180°. ✓

Angle *ABF* = 70° ✓

Marking guidance:

There are several different ways to show that angle *ABF* = 70°. You must make sure you give a clear reason for each step in your working and label your angles correctly to score full marks.

(Total for Question 25 is 4 marks)

26 The diagram shows a logo made from three circles.

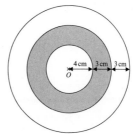

Each circle has centre *O*.

Daisy says that exactly $\frac{1}{3}$ of the logo is shaded.

Is Daisy correct?
You must show all your working.

Area of small circle: $\pi \times 4^2 = 16\pi$
Area of middle circle: $\pi \times 7^2 = 49\pi$
Area of large circle: $\pi \times 10^2 = 100\pi$ ✓

Shaded area = $49\pi - 16\pi = 33\pi$ ✓

Fraction of area shaded = $\frac{33\pi}{100\pi}$ ✓

$\frac{33\pi}{100\pi} = \frac{33}{100}$ which is not equal to $\frac{1}{3}$

Daisy is incorrect because the shaded area is $\frac{33}{100}$ which is not exactly equal to $\frac{1}{3}$ ✓

(Total for Question 26 is 4 marks)

27 The table shows information about the weekly earnings of 20 people who work in a shop.

Weekly earnings (£x)	Frequency
$150 < x \leqslant 250$	1
$250 < x \leqslant 350$	11
$350 < x \leqslant 450$	5
$450 < x \leqslant 550$	0
$550 < x \leqslant 650$	3

(a) Work out an estimate for the mean of the weekly earnings.

Total earned = (200 × 1) + (300 × 11) + (400 × 5) + (500 × 0) + (600 × 3) ✓
= 200 + 3300 + 2000 + 0 + 1800
= 7300

Mean = $\frac{7300}{20}$ = 365 ✓

£ 365 ✓
(3)

Nadiya says,

"The mean may **not** be the best average to use to represent this information."

(b) Do you agree with Nadiya?
You must justify your answer.

Yes, because the mean is affected by outliers. ✓
(1)

(Total for Question 27 is 4 marks)

28 Here is a rectangle.

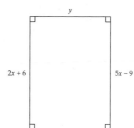

All measurements are in centimetres.

The area of the rectangle is 48 cm².

Show that *y* = 3

$5x - 9 = 2x + 6$ ✓
$5x - 2x - 9 = 6$
$5x - 2x = 6 + 9$
$3x = 15$ ✓
$x = \frac{15}{3}$
$x = 5$

Length of rectangle = $2x + 6 = 2 \times 5 + 6$
= 10 + 6 = 16 ✓

$y = 48 \div 16$ ✓
$y = 3$

(Total for Question 28 is 4 marks)

29 Brogan needs to draw the graph of $y = x^2 + 1$

Here is her graph.

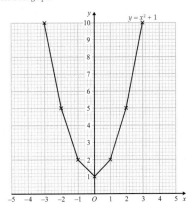

Write down one thing that is wrong with Brogan's graph.

The graph should be a smooth curve, not drawn with straight lines ✓

(Total for Question 29 is 1 mark)

30 In a sale, the normal price of a book is reduced by 30%.
The sale price of the book is £2.80

Work out the normal price of the book.

Sale price = 100% – 30% = 70%

70% = 2.80

$10\% = \dfrac{2.80}{7} = 0.4$ ✓

100% = 0.4 × 10 = 4

£ 4 ✓

(Total for Question 30 is 2 marks)

TOTAL FOR PAPER 1F IS 80 MARKS

82

146